THE PSYCHOLOGY OF INVENTION
IN THE MATHEMATICAL FIELD

AN ESSAY ON

The Psychology of Invention
in the
Mathematical Field

BY

JACQUES HADAMARD

DOVER PUBLICATIONS, INC.,

Library of Congress Catalog Card Number: 54-4731

Manufactured in the United States of America

Dover Publications, Inc.
180 Varick Street
New York 14, N. Y.

A la compagne de ma vie et de mon œuvre.

FOREWORD

*"Je dirai que j'ai trouvé la démonstration de
tel théorème dans telles circonstances; ce
théorème aura un nom barbare, que beaucoup
d'entre vous ne connaîtront pas; mais cela n'a
pas d'importance: ce qui est intéressant pour
le psychologue, ce n'est pas le théorème, ce
sont les circonstances."*

—*Henri Poincaré*

THIS study, like everything which could be written on mathematical invention, was first inspired by Henri Poincaré's famous lecture before the Société de Psychologie in Paris. I first came back to the subject in a meeting at the Centre de Synthèse in Paris (1937). But a more thorough treatment of it has been given in an extensive course of lectures delivered (1943) at the Ecole Libre des Hautes Etudes, New York City.

I wish to express my gratitude to Princeton University Press, for the interest taken in this work and the careful help brought to its publication.

JACQUES HADAMARD

August 21, 1944
New York, N.Y.

CONTENTS

INTRODUCTION

CONCERNING the title of this study, two remarks are useful. We speak of invention: it would be more correct to speak of discovery. The distinction between these two words is well known: discovery concerns a phenomenon, a law, a being which already existed, but had not been perceived. Columbus discovered America: it existed before him; on the contrary, Franklin invented the lightning rod: before him there had never been any lightning rod.

Such a distinction has proved less evident than appears at first glance. Toricelli has observed that when one inverts a closed tube on the mercury trough, the mercury ascends to a certain determinate height: this is a discovery; but, in doing this, he has invented the barometer; and there are plenty of examples of scientific results which are just as much discoveries as inventions. Franklin's invention of the lightning rod is hardly different from his discovery of the electric nature of thunder. This is a reason why the aforesaid distinction does not truly concern us; and, as a matter of fact, psychological conditions are quite the same for both cases.

On the other hand, our title is "Psychology of Invention in the Mathematical Field," and not "Psychology of Mathematical Invention." It may be useful to keep in mind that mathematical invention is but a case of invention in general, a process which can take place in several domains, whether it be in science, literature, in art or also technology.

Modern philosophers even say more. They have perceived that intelligence is perpetual and constant invention, that life is perpetual invention. As Ribot says,[1] "Invention in Fine Arts or Sciences is but a special case. In practical life, in mechanical, military, industrial, commercial inventions, in religious, social, political institutions, the human mind has spent and used as much imagination as anywhere else"; and Bergson,[2] with a still higher and more general intuition, states:

"The inventive effort which is found in all domains of life by the creation of new species has found in mankind alone the means of continuing itself by individuals on whom has been bestowed, along with intelligence, the faculty of initiative, independence and liberty."

Such an audacious comparison has its analogue in Metschnikoff, who observes, at the end of his book on phagocytosis, that, in the human species, the fight against microbes is the work not only of phagocytes, but also of the brain, by creating bacteriology.

One cannot say that various kinds of invention proceed exactly in the same way. As the psychologist Souriau has noticed, there is, between the artistic domain and the scientific one, the difference that art enjoys a greater freedom, since the artist is governed only by his own fantasy, so that works of art are truly inventions. Beethoven's symphonies and even Racine's tragedies are inventions. The scientist behaves quite otherwise and his work properly concerns discoveries. As my master, Hermite, told me: "We are rather servants than masters in Mathematics." Although the truth is not yet known to us, it preexists and

[1] See Delacroix, L'Invention et le Génie (in G. Dumas' *Nouveau Traité de Psychologie*, Vol. VI), p. 449.
[2] *ibid.*, p. 447.

inescapably imposes on us the path we must follow under penalty of going astray.

This does not preclude many analogies between these two activities, as we shall have occasion to observe. These analogies appeared when, in 1937, at the Centre de Synthèse in Paris, a series of lectures was delivered on invention of various kinds, with the help of the great Genevese psychologist, Claparède. A whole week was devoted to the various kinds of invention, with one session for mathematics. Especially, invention in experimental sciences was treated by Louis de Broglie and Bauer, poetical invention by Paul Valéry. The comparison between the circumstances of invention in these various fields may prove very fruitful.

It is all the more useful, perhaps, to deal with a special case such as the mathematical one, which I shall discuss, since it is the one I know best. Results in one sphere (and we shall see that important achievements have been reached in that field, thanks to a masterly lecture of Henri Poincaré) may always be helpful in order to understand what happens in other ones.

I. GENERAL VIEWS AND INQUIRIES

THE SUBJECT we are dealing with is far from unexplored and though, of course, it still holds many mysteries for us, we seem to possess fairly copious data, more copious and more coherent than might have been expected, considering the difficulty of the problem.

That difficulty is not only an intrinsic one, but one which, in an increasing number of instances, hampers the progress of our knowledge: I mean the fact that the subject involves two disciplines, psychology and mathematics, and would require, in order to be treated adequately, that one be both a psychologist and a mathematician. Owing to the lack of this composite equipment, the subject has been investigated by mathematicians on one side, by psychologists on the other and even, as we shall see, by a neurologist.

As always in psychology, two kinds of methods are available: the "subjective" and the "objective" methods.[1] Sub-

[1] I speak of objective or introspective methods. I see that the modern behaviorist distinguishes between objective *psychology* and introspective *psychology* (the latter being said to belong to the past since the death of William James and Titchener), as though these were two different sciences, differing as to their object, while it seems to me that both kinds of methods of observation could be applied and even help each other for the study of the same psychological processes. I understand, however, that for the behaviorist, the object of introspection, i.e., thought and consciousness, is to be ignored.

Already, in older times, the prominent biologist Le Dantec eliminated consciousness by qualifying it as an "epiphenomenon." I have always considered that an unscientific attitude, because if consciousness were an epiphenomenon, it would be the only epiphenomenon in nature, where everything reacts on everything else. But, epiphenomenon or not, it exists and can be observed. We are not unjustified in presenting such observa-

jective (or "introspective") methods are those which
could be called "observing from the inside," that is, those
where information about the ways of thought is directly
obtained by the thinker himself who, looking inwards, reports on his own mental process. The obvious disadvantage
of such a procedure is that the observer may disturb the
very phenomenon which he is investigating. Indeed, as
both operations—to think and to observe one's thought—
are to take place at the same time, it may be supposed a
priori that they are likely to hamper each other. We shall
see, however, that this is less to be feared in the inventive
process (at least, in some of its stages) than in other mental phenomena. In the present study, I shall use the results
of introspection, the only ones I feel qualified to speak of.
In our case, these results are clear enough to deserve, it
would seem, a certain degree of confidence. In doing so,
I face an objection for which I apologize in advance: that
is, the writer is obliged to speak too much about himself.

Objective methods—observing from the outside—are
those in which the experimenter is other than the thinker.
Observation and thought do not interfere with each other;

tions, made by ourselves or by others, as I shall do in the course of this
study.

It must be noticed that most instances considered by behaviorists (I
found them in J. B. Watson's *Behaviorism*) are very different from those
which may concern us, being generally taken from thoughts having a
direct relation with our bodily sensations and which are more easily
interpreted in terms of the doctrine than others. In such cases, cor-
respondences between bodily phenomena and states of consciousness
are easily seen and are more or less known things. They are more hidden for cases of abstract thought, such as those we are going to study;
but there is no reason why they should not be discovered at some future
date. This may happen, for instance, with the help of the electric
waves which accompany cerebral processes (a suggestion which I take
from an article of Henri Laugier in the *Revue Moderne*, reproduced
in his book *Service de France au Canada*).

but on the other hand, only indirect information is thus obtained, the significance of which is not easily seen. One chief reason why they chance to be difficult to employ in our case is because they require the comparison of numerous instances. In agreement with the general principle of experimental science, this would be an essential condition for arriving at the "fact of great yield," as Poincaré says, that is, the fact which penetrates deeply into the nature of the question; but, precisely, these instances cannot be found for such an exceptional phenomenon as invention.

The Mathematics "Bump." Objective methods have generally been applied to invention of any kind, no special investigation being devoted to mathematics. One exception, which we shall very briefly mention, is a curious attempt which has been initiated by the celebrated Gall. It depends on his principle of the so-called "phrenology," that is, on the connection of every mental aptitude with a greater development not only of some part of the brain, but also of the corresponding part of the skull; a rather unhappy idea, as recent neurologists think, of that man who had other very fruitful ones (he was a forerunner of the notion of cerebral localization). According to that principle, mathematical ability ought to be characterized by a special "bump" on the head, the localization of which he actually indicates.

Gall's ideas were taken up (1900)[2] by the neurologist Möbius, who happened to be the grandson of a mathematician, though he himself had no special knowledge of mathematics.

Möbius' book is a rather extensive and thorough study of mathematical ability from the naturalist's standpoint.

2 *Die Anlage zur Mathematik* (Leipzig).

It contains a series of data which, eventually, are likely to
be of interest for that study. They bear, for instance, on
heredity (families of mathematicians),[3] longevity, abilities
of other kinds, etc. Though such an important collection
of data may prove useful at a later date, it seems so far
not to have given rise to any general rule except as concerns the artistic inclinations of mathematicians. (Möbius
confirms the somewhat classic opinion that most mathematicians are fond of music, and asserts that they are also
interested in other arts.)

Now, Möbius agrees with Gall's conclusions in general,
considering, however, in the first place, that the mathematical sign, though always present, may assume a greater
variety of forms than would be understood from Gall's
description.

However, that "bump" hypothesis of Gall-Möbius has
not met with agreement. Anatomists and neurologists
strongly assailed the "Gall redivivus," as they called him,
because Gall's phrenological principle, i.e., conformity of
skull to brain form, is now considered inaccurate.

Let us not insist any longer on this phase of the ques-

[3] There had been, some years earlier (1869), an important work of
Francis Galton on *Hereditary Genius* (London and New York). An
extensive chapter is devoted to men of science.

In connection with the methods to which Möbius' book was generally
devoted, interesting data are contained in Leonard George Guthrie's
Contributions to the Study of Precocity in Children, concerning early
inclinations of prominent men. To speak only of mathematicians,
Galilei's first calling was toward painting, after which, when seventeen,
he began to study medicine, and only later mathematics. William
Herschell's first education was as a musician. Besides, it is known that
Gauss hesitated between mathematics and philology.

Similar instances exist as concerns contemporary men. I heard from
Paul Painlevé himself that he hesitated greatly between devoting himself
to mathematics or to political life. He at first adopted the former
activity, but, as is well known, finally engaged in both of them.

tion, which is to be left to specialists. But it is not useless
to speak of it from the mathematical standpoint. From
that point of view also, some objections can be raised, at
least at a first glance, against the very principle of such
research. It is more than doubtful that there exists one
definite "mathematical aptitude." Mathematical creation
and mathematical intelligence are not without connection
with creation in general and with general intelligence. It
rarely happens, in high schools, that the pupil who is first
in mathematics is the last in other branches of learning;
and, to consider a higher level, a great proportion of
prominent mathematicians have been creators in other
fields. One of the greatest, Gauss, carried out important
and classical experiments on magnetism; and Newton's
fundamental discoveries in optics are well known. Was the
shape of the head of Descartes or Leibniz influenced by
their mathematical abilities or by their philosophical
ones?

Also there is a counterpart. We shall see that there is
not just one single category of mathematical minds, but
several kinds, the differences being important enough
to make it doubtful that all such minds correspond to
one and the same characteristic of the brain.

All this would not be contradictory to the principle of
Gall interpreted in a general way, i.e., to interdependence
of the mathematical functioning of the mind with the
physiology and anatomy of the brain; but the first application of it which Gall and Möbius proposed does not seem
to be justified.

Generally speaking, we must admit that mental faculties
which seem at first to be simple are composite in an unexpected way. It has been recognized by objective methods

(observation of the effects of wounds or other injuries of
the head) that such is the case with the best known faculty
of all, the language faculty, which consists of several
different ones. There are cerebral localizations, as Gall
had announced, but without such simple and precise cor-
respondences as he supposed.

There is every reason to think that the mathematical
faculty must be at least as composite as has been found
for the faculty of language. Though, of course, decisive
documents are not and will probably never be available
in the former case as they are in the latter, observations
on the one phenomenon may help us to understand the
other.

Psychologists' Views on the Subject. Many psychologists have also meditated not especially on mathematical invention, but on invention in general. Among them, I shall
mention only two names, Souriau and Paulhan. These two
psychologists show a contrast in their opinions. Souriau
(1881) was, it seems, the first to have maintained that
invention occurs by pure chance, while Paulhan (1901)[4]
remains faithful to the more classic theory of logic and
systematic reasoning. There is also a difference in method,
which can hardly be accounted for by the small difference
in the dates, for while Paulhan has taken much information
from scientists and other inventors, there is hardly any
to be found in Souriau's work. It is curious that, operating
thus, Souriau is led to some very shrewd and accurate
remarks; but, on the other hand, he has not avoided one
or two serious errors which we shall have to mention.

Later on, a most important study in that line was

---

[4] Souriau, *Théorie de l'Invention* (Paris, 1881). Paulhan, *Psychologie
de l'Invention.*

conducted (1937) at the Centre de Synthèse in Paris, as mentioned in the introduction.

Mathematical Inquiries. Let us come to mathematicians. One of them, Maillet, started a first inquiry as to their methods of work. One famous question, in particular, was already raised by him: that of the "mathematical dream," it having been suggested often that the solution of problems that have defied investigation may appear in dreams.

Though not asserting the absolute non-existence of "mathematical dreams," Maillet's inquiry shows that they cannot be considered as having a serious significance. Only one remarkable observation is reported by the prominent American mathematician, Leonard Eugene Dickson, who can positively assert its accuracy. His mother and her sister, who, at school, were rivals in geometry, had spent a long and futile evening over a certain problem. During the night, his mother dreamed of it and began developing the solution in a loud and clear voice; her sister, hearing that, arose and took notes. On the following morning in class, she happened to have the right solution which Dickson's mother failed to know.

This observation, an important one on account of the personality of the relator and the certitude with which it is reported, is a most extraordinary one. Except for that very curious case, most of the 69 correspondents who answered Maillet on that question never experienced any mathematical dream (I never did) or, in that line, dreamed of wholly absurd things, or were unable to state precisely the question they happened to dream of. Five dreamed of quite naive arguments. There is one more positive answer; but it is difficult to take account of it, as its author remains anonymous.

Besides, in that matter, there is a confusion which raises grave doubts. One phenomenon is certain and I can vouch for its absolute certainty: the sudden and immediate appearance of a solution at the very moment of sudden awakening. On being very abruptly awakened by an external noise, a solution[5] long searched for appeared to me at once without the slightest instant of reflection on my part—the fact was remarkable enough to have struck me unforgettably—and in a quite different direction from any of those which I had previously tried to follow. Of course, such a phenomenon, which is fully certain in my own case, could be easily confused with a "mathematical dream," from which it differs.

I shall not dwell any longer on Maillet's inquiry because a more important one was started, a few years later, by some mathematicians with the help of Claparède and another prominent Genevese psychologist, Flournoy, and published in the periodical *L'Enseignement Mathématique*. An extensive questionnaire was sent out, consisting of a few more than 30 questions (See Appendix I). These questions (including "mathematical dream") belonged to both classes of investigation methods which we have already differentiated, some of them being "objective" (as much as a questionnaire can be). For instance, mathematicians were asked whether they were influenced by noises and to what extent, or by meteorological circumstances, whether literary or artistic courses of thought were considered useful or harmful.

Other questions were of a more introspective character

[5] For technicians, the beginning of No. 27 (pp. 199-200) in *Journal de Mathématiques pures et appliquées*, Series 4, Vol. IX, 1898 (valuation of a determinant).

and penetrated more directly and deeply into the nature of the subject. Authors were asked whether they were deeply interested in reading the works of their predecessors or, on the contrary, preferred to study problems directly by themselves; whether they were in the habit of abandoning a problem for a while to resume it again only later on (which I, personally, do in many cases and which I always recommend to beginners who consult me). Above all, they were asked what they could say on the genesis of their chief discoveries.

Some Criticisms. Reading that questionnaire, one may notice the lack of some questions, even when analogous to some which have actually been asked. For instance, when asking mathematicians whether they indulged in music or poetry, the questionnaire did not mention possible interest in sciences other than mathematics. Especially, biology, as Hermite used to observe, may be a most useful study even for mathematicians, as hidden and eventually fruitful analogies may appear between processes in both kinds of study.

Similarly, when inquiring about the influence of meteorological circumstances or the existence of periods of exaltation or depression, no more precise question was asked concerning the influence of the psychical state of the worker and especially the emotions which he may be experiencing. This question is all the more interesting because it has been taken up by Paul Valéry in a lecture at the French Society of Philosophy, in which he suggested that emotions are evidently likely to influence poetical production. Now, however likely it may seem at first glance that some kind of emotions may favor poetry because they more or less directly find their expression in poetry, it is not certain that this reason is the right one or at least the only one. Indeed, I know by personal experience that powerful emotions may favor entirely different kinds of mental creation (e.g., the mathematical one[1]); and in this connection, I should agree with this curious statement of Daunou: "In Sciences, even the most rigid ones, no truth is born of the genius of an Archimedes or a Newton without a poetical emotion and some quivering of intelligent nature."

Moreover, the most essential question—I mean the one which concerns the genesis of discovery—suggests another one, which is not mentioned in the questionnaire though its interest is obvious. Mathematicians are asked how they have succeeded. Now, there are not only successes but also failures, and the reasons for failures would be at least as important to know.

This is in relation to the most important criticism which can be formulated against such inquiries as Maillet's or Claparède and Flournoy's: indeed, such inquiries are subject to a cause of error which they can hardly avoid. Who can be considered a mathematician, especially a mathematician whose creative processes are worthy of interest? Most of the answers which reached the inquirers come from alleged mathematicians whose names are now completely unknown. This explains why they could not be asked for the reasons of their failures, which only first-rate men would dare to speak of. In the above mentioned inquiries, I could hardly find one or two significant names, such as the physico-mathematician Boltzmann. Such

[1] The above mentioned finding of a solution on a sudden awakening occurred during such a period of emotion.

masters as Appell, Darboux, Picard, Painlevé sent no
answers, which was perhaps a mistake on their part.

Since most answers to the inquiries of Maillet and of
the *Enseignement Mathématique* were of slight interest
for that reason, it occurred to me to submit some of the
questions to a man whose mathematical creation is one of
the most audacious and penetrating, Jules Drach. Some
of his answers were especially suggestive, in the first place,
as concerns biology in which, like Hermite, he takes much
interest and, chiefly, on the study of previous discoverers.
This is a question where it appears that even among men
who are born mathematicians, important mental differences may exist. The historians of the amazing life of
Evariste Galois have revealed to us that, according to the
testimony of one of his schoolfellows, even from his high
school time, he hated reading treatises on algebra, because
he failed to find in them the characteristic traits of inventors. Now, Mr. Drach, whose work, besides, is closely
related to Galois', has the same way of approach. He always wishes to refer to the very form in which discoveries
have appeared to their authors. On the contrary, most
mathematicians who have answered Claparède and Flournoy's inquiry prefer, when studying any previous work, to
think it out and rediscover it by themselves. This is my
approach, so that finally I know, in any case, of only one
inventor, who is myself.

Poincaré's Statements. Again, we shall put aside the inquiry of the *Enseignement Mathématique*. While it failed,
as we have said, to distinguish adequately between those
who replied, it did, on the other hand, provoke, somewhat
later, a testimony which was the most authoritative one
could wish to obtain. Conditions of invention have been

investigated by the greatest genius which our science has
known during the last half century, by the man whose
impulse is felt throughout contemporary mathematical
science. I allude to the celebrated lecture of Henri Poincaré at the Société de Psychologie in Paris.[6] Poincaré's
observations throw a resplendent light on relations between the conscious and the unconscious, between the logical and the fortuitous which lie at the base of the problem.
Notwithstanding possible objections which will be discussed in due time, the conclusions which he reaches in
that lecture seem to me fully justified and, at least in the
first five sections, I shall follow him[7] throughout.

Poincaré's example is taken from one of his greatest
discoveries, the first which has consecrated his glory, the
theory of fuchsian groups and fuchsian functions. In the
first place, I must take Poincaré's own precaution and
state that we shall have to use technical terms without the
reader's needing to understand them. "I shall say, for
example," he says, "that I have found the demonstration
of such a theorem under such circumstances. This theorem
will have a barbarous name, unfamiliar to many, but that is
unimportant; what is of interest for the psychologist is
not the theorem, but the circumstances."[8]

So, we are going to speak of fuchsian functions. At first,
Poincaré attacked the subject vainly for a fortnight, at-

[6] "Mathematical Creation," in *The Foundations of Science*. Translated
by G. Bruce Halsted (New York: The Science Press, 1913), p. 387.

[7] Quotations without an author's name which will be found in the
following pages are taken from Poincaré's lecture.

[8] Poincaré deals with the case of mathematics. As Dr. de Saussure,
to whom I am indebted for various interesting remarks, suggested
to me, independence between the process of invention and the invented
thing may be less in more concrete subjects (see below, Section IX,
p. 131).

tempting to prove that there could not be any such functions: an idea which was going to prove to be a false one.

Indeed, during a night of sleeplessness and under conditions to which we shall come back, he builds up one first class of those functions. Then he wishes to find an expression for them.

"I wanted to represent these functions by the quotient of two series; this idea was perfectly conscious and deliberate; the analogy with elliptic functions guided me. I asked myself what properties these series must have if they existed, and succeeded without difficulty in forming the series I have called thetafuchsian.

"Just at this time, I left Caen, where I was living, to go on a geologic excursion under the auspices of the School of Mines. The incidents of the travel made me forget my mathematical work. Having reached Coutances, we entered an omnibus to go some place or other. At the moment when I put my foot on the step, the idea came to me, without anything in my former thoughts seeming to have paved the way for it, that the transformations I had used to define the Fuchsian functions were identical with those of non-Euclidian geometry. I did not verify the idea; I should not have had time, as, upon taking my seat in the omnibus, I went on with a conversation already commenced, but I felt a perfect certainty. On my return to Caen, for conscience' sake, I verified the result at my leisure.

"Then I turned my attention to the study of some arithmetical questions apparently without much success and without a suspicion of any connection with my preceding researches. Disgusted with my failure, I went to spend a few days at the seaside and thought of something else. One morning, walking on the bluff, the idea came to me, with just the same characteristics of brevity, suddenness and immediate certainty, that the arithmetic transformations of indefinite ternary quadratic forms were identical with those of non-Euclidian geometry."

These two results showed to Poincaré that there existed other fuchsian groups and, consequently, other fuchsian functions than those which he had found during his sleeplessness. The latter constituted only a special case: the question was to investigate the most general ones. In this he was stopped by most serious difficulties, which a persistent conscious effort allowed him to define more adequately, but not, at first, to overcome. Then, again, the solution appeared to him as unexpectedly, as unpreparedly as in the other two instances, while he was serving his time in the army.

And he adds: "Most striking at first is this appearance of sudden illumination, a manifest sign of long, unconscious prior work. The role of this unconscious work in mathematical invention appears to me incontestable."

Looking at One's Own Unconsciousness. Before examining the latter conclusion, let us resume the history of that sleepless night which initiated all that memorable work, and which we set aside in the beginning because it offered very special characteristics.

"One evening," Poincaré says, "contrary to my custom, I drank black coffee and could not sleep. Ideas rose in crowds; I felt them collide until pairs interlocked, so to speak, making a stable combination."

That strange phenomenon is perhaps the more interesting for the psychologist because it is more exceptional. Poincaré lets us know that it is rather frequent as concerns himself: "It seems, in such cases, that one is present at his own unconscious work, made partially perceptible to the over-excited consciousness, yet without having changed its nature. Then we vaguely comprehend what distinguishes the two mechanisms or, if you wish, the working methods of the two egos."

But that extraordinary fact of watching passively, as if from the outside, the evolution of subconscious ideas seems to be quite special to him. I have never experienced that marvelous sensation, nor have I ever heard of its happening to others.

Instances in Other Fields. What he reports in the remainder of his lecture is, on the contrary, absolutely general and common to every student of research. Thus Gauss, referring to an arithmetical theorem which he had unsuccessfully tried to prove for years, writes: "Finally, two days ago, I succeeded, not on account of my painful efforts, but by the grace of God. Like a sudden flash of lightning, the riddle happened to be solved. I myself cannot say what was the conducting thread which connected what I previously knew with what made my success possible."[8a]

It is unnecessary to observe that what happened to me on my awakening is perfectly similar and typical, as the solution which appeared to me: (1) was without any relation to my attempts of former days, so that it could not have been elaborated by my previous conscious work; (2) appeared without any time for thought, however brief.

The same character of suddenness and spontaneousness had been pointed out, some years earlier, by another great scholar of contemporary science. Helmholtz reported it in an important speech delivered in 1896. Since Helmholtz and Poincaré, it has been recognized by psychologists as

[8a] Letter mentioned in *Revue des questions scientifiques*, October 1886, p. 575.

being very general in every kind of invention. Graham
Wallas, in his *Art of Thought*, suggested calling it "illumination," this illumination being generally preceded by
an "incubation" stage wherein the study seems to be completely interrupted and the subject dropped. Such an
illumination is even mentioned in several replies on the inquiry of *L'Enseignement Mathématique*. Other physicists
like Langevin, chemists like Ostwald, tell us of having experienced it. In quite different fields, let us cite a couple
of instances. One has attracted the attention of the psychologist Paulhan. It is a celebrated letter of Mozart:[8b]

"When I feel well and in a good humor, or when I am
taking a drive or walking after a good meal, or in the
night when I cannot sleep, thoughts crowd into my mind
as easily as you could wish. Whence and how do they come?
I do not know and I have nothing to do with it. Those which
please me, I keep in my head and hum them; at least others
have told me that I do so. Once I have my theme, another
melody comes, linking itself to the first one, in accordance
with the needs of the composition as a whole: the counter-
point, the part of each instrument, and all these melodic
fragments at last produce the entire work. Then my soul
is on fire with inspiration, if however nothing occurs to
distract my attention. The work grows; I keep expanding
it, conceiving it more and more clearly until I have the
entire composition finished in my head though it may be
long. Then my mind seizes it as a glance of my eye a beautiful picture or a handsome youth. It does not come to me
successively, with its various parts worked out in detail, as
they will be later on, but it is in its entirety that my imagination lets me hear it.

"Now, how does it happen, that, while I am at work, my

[8b] See Paulhan, *Psychologie de l'invention*, p. 97, who refers to Seailles,
Le Génie dans l'art, p. 177.

compositions assume the form or the style which characterize Mozart and are not like anybody else's? Just as it
happens that my nose is big and hooked, Mozart's nose and
not another man's. I do not aim at originality and I should
be much at a loss to describe my style. It is quite natural
that people who really have something particular about
them should be different from each other on the outside as
well as on the inside."

Poetical inspiration is reported to have been as spontaneous with Lamartine who happened to compose verses
instantly, without one moment of reflection; and we have
the following most suggestive statement made at the
French Philosophical Society by our great poet Paul
Valéry:[8c] "In this process, there are two stages.

"There is that one where the man whose business is writing experiences a kind of flash—for this intellectual life,
anything but passive, is really made of fragments; it is
in a way composed of elements very brief, yet felt to
be very rich in possibilities, which do not illuminate the
whole mind, which indicate to the mind, rather, that there
are forms completely new which it is sure to be able
to possess after a certain amount of work. Sometimes I
have observed this moment when a sensation arrives at
the mind; it is as a gleam of light, not so much illuminating as dazzling. This arrival calls attention, points, rather
than illuminates, and in fine, is itself an enigma which carries with it the assurance that it can be postponed. You say,
'I see, and then tomorrow I shall see more.' There is an
activity, a special sensitization; soon you will go into the
dark-room and the picture will be seen to emerge.

"I do not affirm that this is well described, for it is extremely hard to describe. . . ."

[8c] *Bulletin Soc. Philosophie*, Vol. 28, 1928.

Similarly, as Catherine Patrick has noticed in the article cited below, footnote 10 to Section III, the English poet A. E. Housman in a lecture delivered at Cambridge, England (see his valuable booklet *The Name and Nature of Poetry*) also describes that spontaneous and almost involuntary creation, eventually alternating with conscious effort.

Similar observations occur even in ordinary life. Does it not frequently happen that the name of a person or of a place which you have vainly tried to remember, recurs to you when you are no longer thinking of it?

That this fact is more analogous to the process of invention than would be believed at first is shown by a remark of Remy de Gourmont: he notices that the right word to express an idea is also very often, after long and fruitless search, found in the same way, viz., when one is thinking of something else. This case is interesting as it presents an intermediate character, being obviously analogous to the preceding one and nevertheless already belonging to the field of invention.

No less similar to the above observation is the well-known proverb: "Sleep on it." This again may be considered as belonging to the realm of invention if we follow modern philosophers and take the word in a broad sense, as we said in the Introduction.

The Chance Hypothesis. The biologist Nicolle[9] also mentions creative inspirations and even strongly insists on them. But it is necessary to discuss the way in which he interprets them.

For Poincaré, as we saw, they are evident manifestations

---

[9] *Biologie de l'Invention*, pp. 5-7.

of a previous unconscious work, and here I must say that I do not see how this view can be seriously disputed.

However, Nicolle does not seem to agree with it; or, more exactly, he does not speak of the unconscious. "The inventor," he writes, "does not know prudence nor its junior sister, slowness. He does not sound the ground nor quibble. He at once jumps into the unexplored domain and by this sole act, he conquers it. By a streak of lightning, the hitherto obscure problem, which no ordinary feeble lamp would have revealed, is at once flooded with light. It is like a creation. Contrary to progressive acquirements, such an act owes nothing to logic or to reason. The act of discovery is an accident."

This is, in its most extreme form, the theory of chance which psychologists like Souriau also set forth.

Not only can I not accept it, but I can hardly understand how a scientist like Nicolle could have conceived of such an idea. Whatever respect we must have for the great personality of Charles Nicolle, explanation by *pure* chance is equivalent to no explanation at all and to asserting that there are effects without causes. Would Nicolle have been contented to say that diphtheria—or typhus, which he so admirably investigated—are the result of pure chance? Even if we do not, at this juncture, enter into the analysis which we shall try to give in the next section, chance is chance: that is, it is the same for Nicolle or Poincaré or for the man in the street. Chance cannot explain that the discovery of the cause of typhus was made by Nicolle (that is, by a man having pondered scientific subjects and the conditions of experiments for years and also having shown his marvellous ability) rather than by any of his nurses. And as to Poincaré, if chance could explain one of the brilliant intuitions which he describes in his lecture—which I cannot even believe—how would that explanation account for all those which he successively mentions, not to speak of all those which have occurred throughout the various theories which constitute his immense work and have transformed almost every branch of mathematical science? You could as well imagine, according to well-known comparison, a monkey striking a typewriter and fortuitously printing the American Constitution.

This does not mean that chance has no role in the inventing process.[10] Chance does act. We shall see in Section III how it acts inside unconsciousness.

---

[10] Dealing with the mathematical domain, we speak only of *psychological* chance, i.e., fortuitous mental processes. As Claparède points out (Meetings of 1937 at the Centre de Synthèse), it must be distinguished from *external* hazards, such as occur in the well-known case of Galvani's frogs and which, of course, are likely to play the initial role in experimental discovery.

II. DISCUSSIONS ON UNCONSCIOUSNESS

THOUGH unconsciousness is, strictly speaking, a business of professional psychologists, it is so closely connected with my main subject that I cannot help dealing scantily with it.

That those sudden enlightenments which can be called inspirations cannot be produced by chance alone is already evident by what we have said: there can be no doubt of the necessary intervention of some previous mental process unknown to the inventor, in other terms, of an unconscious one. Indeed, after having seen, as we shall at many places in the following, the unconscious at work, any doubt as to its existence can hardly arise.

Although observations in everyday life show us this existence, and although it has been recognized since the time of St. Augustine and by masters such as Leibniz, the unconscious has by no means remained unquestioned. The very fact that it is unknown to the usual self gives to it such an appearance of mystery that it has experienced, at the hands of various authors, equally excessive disgraces and favors. Several authors have been stubbornly opposed to admitting any unconscious phenomenon. To speak of a case directly connected with invention, it is difficult to understand how, as late as 1852, after centuries of psychological studies, one could read in a work on invention,[1] such a statement as the following: "These seeming divinations, these almost immediate conclusions are to be explained most naturally by known laws[?]: mind thinks either by analogy or by habit; thus, mind jumps over intermedi-

[1] Desdouits, *Theorie de l'Invention.*

aries," as though the fact of jumping over intermediaries which one cannot but know of were not, by definition, an unconscious mental process! One cannot help remembering Pierre Janet's patients, who, obeying his suggestion, "did not see" the cards which were marked with a cross . . . which, however, they must necessarily have seen in order to eliminate them. But, of course, Pierre Janet's conclusion was not to deny unconsciousness, whose intervention is, in such cases, grossly evident.

In order to ignore unconscious ideas by any means, the philosopher Alfred Fouillée uses two contrary attitudes: either he will contend that, under any conditions, there must be consciousness, only very feeble and indistinct; or, if this hypothesis does not give him a means to avoid the one he seems to be afraid of, he withdraws in the opposite direction by invoking reflex actions, i.e., such actions the existence of which has been undoubtedly recognized by physiologists operating, for instance, on beheaded frogs, and which do not imply the intervention of mental centers but only of more or less peripheral and inferior nervous elements.

There are many well-known acts of mind which do not admit of either one or the other of these opposite explanations. Let us only mention the so-called "automatic writing," which has been thoroughly studied in the case of some psychical patients, but which is by no means an exclusive feature of such abnormal people. Many of us, if not all of us, have experienced automatic writing; at least I have very often in my life. Once, when I was in the high school and had before me a task which did not interest me very much, I suddenly perceived that I had written at the top of my sheet of paper "Mathématiques." Could that be considered as a reflex motion? Can such reflex motions imply the rather complicated gestures of handwriting; and are the corresponding inferior centers aware that "Mathématiques" wants an "h" after the "t"? On the other hand, if I had given one instant's thought, however short, to what I was writing, I should never have written that word, as the paper was devoted to a quite different subject.

The Manifold Character of Unconsciousness. Today, the existence of the unconsciousness seems to be rather generally admitted, although some philosophical schools still wish to exclude it.

Indeed, very ordinary facts illustrate with full evidence not only the intervention of unconscious phenomena, but one of their important properties: I allude to the familiar —which does not mean simple—fact of recognizing a human face. Identifying a person you know requires the help of hundreds of features, not a single one of which you could explicitly mention (if not especially gifted or trained for drawing). Nevertheless, all these characters of the face of your friend must be present in your mind—in your unconscious mind, of course—and all of them must be present at the same instant. Therefore, we see that the unconscious has the important property of being manifold; several and probably many things can and do occur in it simultaneously. This contrasts with the conscious ego which is unique.

We also see that this multiplicity of the unconscious enables it to carry out a work of synthesis. In the above case, the numerous details of a physiognomy result, for our consciousness, in only one sensation, viz., recognition.[2]

---

[2] I understand that, in the contemporary Gestalt psychology, there is a unique sensation of physiognomy, independent of the ideas of the various

Fringe-Consciousness. Not only is it impossible to doubt the reality of the unconscious, but we must emphasize that there is hardly any operation of our mind which does not imply it. At a first glance, ideas are never in a more positively conscious state than when we express them in speaking. However, when I pronounce one sentence, where is the following one? Certainly not in the field of my consciousness, which is occupied by sentence number one; and nevertheless, I do think of it, and it is ready to appear the next instant, which cannot occur if I do not think of it unconsciously. But, in that case, we have to deal with an unconscious which is very superficial, quite near to consciousness and at its immediate disposal.

It seems that we can identify this with what Francis Galton[3] calls the "ante-chamber" of consciousness, beautifully describing it as follows:

details. I am not qualified to discuss that important conception; however, as the question is closely connected with what we are going to say later on (especially in Section VI), I must state precisely that whether we admit it or not, there is certainly something corresponding to the individual effect of light on each point of our retina (at least at the very first moment when this effect is transmitted to the brain) and that these individual sensations are unconscious. Is that unconsciousness—generally a very remote one, probably because the corresponding mechanism has been acquired in earliest childhood—analogous to those which will interest us in the following sections? This would be another question; but I must add that this identity of nature is hardly doubtful for me: there is a chain of intermediaries, some of which are even described by the Gestaltists themselves (as I see by Paul Guillaume's *Psychologie de la Forme*) and above all, such cases as learning to ride a bicycle (as has been noticed by several authors). Personally, having learned that when an adult, I did not master it until everything, from having been conscious in the beginning, became fully unconscious—so fully unconscious that I hardly knew why my motions had a better success finally than originally.

[3] *Inquiries into Human Faculty,* p. 203 of the first edition, 1883 (London, New York: Macmillan); p. 146 of the 1908 edition (London: J. M. Dent; New York: E. P. Dutton).

"When I am engaged in trying to think anything out, the process of doing so appears to me to be this: The ideas that lie at any moment within my full consciousness seem to attract of their own accord the most appropriate out of a number of other ideas that are lying close at hand, but imperfectly within the range of my consciousness. There seems to be a presence-chamber in my mind where full consciousness holds court, and where two or three ideas are at the same time in audience, and an ante-chamber full of more or less allied ideas, which is situated just beyond the full ken of consciousness. Out of this ante-chamber the ideas most nearly allied to those in the presence-chamber appear to be summoned in a mechanically logical way, and to have their turn of audience."

The word "subconsciousness" might be distinguished from "unconsciousness" in order to denote such superficial unconscious processes and there is, moreover, the word "fringe-consciousness," created by William James and then used by Wallas with that same meaning, as much as I understand, and which is even very expressive in that sense.[4] These subconscious states are valuable for psychology by being accessible to introspection, which, at least in general,[5] is not possible for more remote processes. Indeed, it is thanks to them that introspection is possible. To describe them, psychologists such as Wallas use a comparison drawn from the facts of eyesight. "The field of vision of our eyes consists of a small circle of full or 'focal'

---

[4] "Foreconscious," used by Varendonck and other writers of Freud's school for special psychic states, is doubtfully available for us.

[5] An exception is Poincaré's sleepless night: see p. 14. Another one possibly (though less certainly) occurred in the case of a technical inventor mentioned by Claparède in the meeting of the Centre de Synthèse.

vision, surrounded by an irregular area of peripheral vision, which is increasingly vague and imperfect as the limit of vision is neared. We are usually unaware of the existence of our peripheral vision, because as soon as anything interesting presents itself there we have a strong natural tendency to turn the focus of vision in its direction. Using these terms, we can say that one reason why we tend to ignore the mental events in our peripheral consciousness is that we have a strong tendency to bring them into focal consciousness as soon as they are interesting to us, but that we can sometimes, by a severe effort, keep them in the periphery of consciousness, and there observe them."

The observation of the distinction between consciousness and fringe-consciousness is generally difficult; but the difficulty happens to be much less in the case of invention, which interests us. The reason for that is that invention work by itself implies that thought be inflexibly directed toward the solution of the problem: when obtaining the latter, and only then, the mind can perceive what takes place in the "fringe-consciousness," a fact which will be of a great interest to us in this study.

Successive Layers in the Unconscious. We see that there are at least two kinds—more precisely, two degrees—of unconsciousness.

It can hardly be doubted, and we shall be able to confirm this later on, that there must even be, in the unconscious, several successive layers, the most superficial one being the one we just considered. More remote is the unconscious layer which acts in automatic writing; still more those which allow inspirations such as we reported in the preceding section. Even deeper ones will appear to us at the end of this study. There seems to be a kind of con-

tinuity between full consciousness and more and more hidden levels of the unconscious: a succession which seems to be
especially well described in Taine's book *On Intelligence*,
when he writes:[6]

"You may compare the mind of a man to the stage of a
theatre, very narrow at the footlights but constantly
broadening as it goes back. At the footlights, there is
hardly room for more than one actor. . . . As one goes
further and further away from the footlights, there are
other figures less and less distinct as they are more distant
from the lights. And beyond these groups, in the wings and
altogether in the background, are innumerable obscure
shapes that a sudden call may bring forward and even
within direct range of the footlights. Undefined evolutions
constantly take place throughout this seething mass of
actors of all kinds, to furnish the chorus leaders who in
turn, as in a magic lantern picture, pass before our eyes."[7]

That striking description is quite similar to the Book X
of St. Augustine's *Confessions*. Only St. Augustine speaks
of memory; but, as it seems to me, he fully realizes the—for
me—undoubted fact that memory belongs to the domain
of the unconscious.

Fringe-subconscious evidently offers some analogy with
the very vaguely conscious ideas which Fouillée supposes,
while, at the other end of the chain, the succession of un-

[6] Added by Taine for the first time in the edition of 1897 (Vol. I),
p. 278.

[7] Some recent psychological schools, such as Freud's, would seem, at
first, to disagree with the above point of view and to speak only of one
kind of (proper) unconscious. As I am informed by a competent colleague and friend, this would be a misinterpretation of Freud's thought.

We already have seen (Note 2, p. 23) that ideas have a tendency
to become more and more unconscious by influence of time: a circumstance we shall again meet with in Section VII (see p. 101).

conscious layers is more probably, as Spencer states (*The Principles of Psychology*, Vol. I, Chap. IV), in continuity with reflex phenomena. Thus, the two states which Fouillée wants to oppose to unconsciousness seem to be nothing else than the extreme cases of it: a double conclusion, which, however, Fouillée rejects (*L'Evolutionisme des Idées-Forces*, Introduction, p. xiv and end of p. xix) by arguments the discussion of which it is useless to inflict upon the reader.

III. THE UNCONSCIOUS AND DISCOVERY

Combination of Ideas. What we just observed concerning the unconscious in general will be seen again from another angle, when speaking of its relations with discovery.

We shall see a little later that the possibility of imputing discovery to pure chance is already excluded by Poincaré's observations, when more attentively considered.

On the contrary, that there is an intervention of chance but also a necessary work of unconsciousness, the latter implying and not contradicting the former, appears, as Poincaré shows, when we take account not merely of the results of introspection, but of the very nature of the question.

Indeed, it is obvious that invention or discovery, be it in mathematics or anywhere else, takes place by combining ideas.[1] Now, there is an extremely great number of such combinations, most of which are devoid of interest, while, on the contrary, very few of them can be fruitful. Which ones does our mind—I mean our conscious mind—perceive? Only the fruitful ones, or exceptionally, some which could be fruitful.

However, to find these, it has been necessary to construct the very numerous possible combinations, among which the useful ones are to be found.

It cannot be avoided that this first operation take place,

[1] Max Müller observes that the Latin verb "cogito," for "to think," etymologically means "to shake together." St. Augustine had already noticed that and also observed that "intelligo" means to "select among," in a curious connection with what we say in the text.

to a certain extent, at random, so that the role of chance is hardly doubtful in this first step of the mental process. But we see that that intervention of chance occurs inside the unconscious: for most of these combinations—more exactly, all those which are useless—remain unknown to us.

Moreover, this shows us again the manifold character of the unconscious, which is necessary to construct those numerous combinations and to compare them with each other.

The Following Step. It is obvious that this first process, this building up of numerous combinations, is only the beginning of creation, even, as we should say, preliminary to it. As we just saw, and as Poincaré observes, to create consists precisely in not making useless combinations and in examining only those which are useful and which are only a small minority. Invention is discernment, choice.

To Invent Is to Choose. This very remarkable conclusion appears the more striking if we compare it with what Paul Valéry writes in the *Nouvelle Revue Française*: "It takes two to invent anything. The one makes up combinations; the other one chooses, recognizes what he wishes and what is important to him in the mass of the things which the former has imparted to him.

"What we call genius is much less the work of the first one than the readiness of the second one to grasp the value of what has been laid before him and to choose it."

We see how beautifully the mathematician and the poet agree in that fundamental view of invention consisting of a choice.

Esthetics in Invention. How can such a choice be made? The rules which must guide it "are extremely fine and delicate. It is almost impossible to state them precisely;

they are felt rather than formulated. Under these conditions, how can we imagine a sieve capable of applying them mechanically?"

Though we do not directly see this sieve at work, we can answer the question, because we are aware of the results it affords, i.e., the combinations of ideas which are perceived by our conscious mind. This result is not doubtful. "The privileged unconscious phenomena, those susceptible of becoming conscious, are those which, directly or indirectly, affect most profoundly our emotional sensibility.

"It may be surprising to see emotional sensibility invoked à propos of mathematical demonstrations which, it would seem, can interest only the intellect. This would be to forget the feeling of mathematical beauty, of the harmony of numbers and forms, of geometric elegance. This is a true esthetic feeling that all real mathematicians know, and surely it belongs to emotional sensibility."

That an affective element is an essential part in every discovery or invention is only too evident, and has been insisted upon by several thinkers; indeed, it is clear that no significant discovery or invention can take place without the *will* of finding. But with Poincaré, we see something else, the intervention of the sense of beauty playing its part as an indispensable *means* of finding. We have reached the double conclusion:

> that invention is choice
> that this choice is imperatively governed by the
> sense of scientific beauty.

Coming Back to the Unconscious. In what region—a word not to be taken in a too literal, but, so to say, in a symbolic meaning—in what region of the mind does that sorting take place? Surely not in consciousness,[2] which, among all possible combinations, only knows of the right ones.

Poincaré, at first, sets forth the idea that the unconscious itself should exclusively perceive the interesting combinations. He does not insist on that first hypothesis and, indeed, I cannot consider it as deserving further examination. It is, as it seems, nothing but recording before making a second jump and would be only a verbal question, a question of definition: we should have to find in what "region" uninteresting combinations could be eliminated, and there would be no reason not to call that other region, if existing, another part of the unconscious.

So there remains only Poincaré's final conclusion, viz., that to the unconscious belongs not only the complicated task of constructing the bulk of various combinations of ideas, but also the most delicate and essential one of selecting those which satisfy our sense of beauty and, consequently, are likely to be useful.

Other Views on Incubation. These a priori reasons would be by themselves sufficient to justify Poincaré's conclusion. However, that conclusion has been assailed by various authors, some of whom[3] again seem to be moved by that same

[2] Mozart's letter (see p. 16) suggests that, in his mind, choice is partly conscious, though probably, as we should think, preceded by a preliminary unconscious one: otherwise we should be re-conducted to the hypothesis of pure chance.

[3] Rossman (*Psychology of the Inventor*, VI, p. 86) writes: "The assumption that the subconscious is responsible for the final condition is no answer to the problem. It merely amounts to giving a name to a thing which puzzles and mystifies us." Now, unconscious phenomena are not mere names, but realities. Though they are less easy to observe directly, they exist, as we have seen, whether they are the cause of illumination or not. To invoke "physiological and chemical conditions in the body," as the author does—without trying, of course, to specify

fear of the unconscious which we met with in the preceding section. Let us see how they endeavor to account for the striking fact of illumination.

It is not necessary to speak again of the doctrine of pure chance, which we have discussed in Section I and at the beginning of this one. Therefore, we consider it as granted that incubation generally precedes illumination.[4] In this period of incubation, no work of the mind is consciously perceived; but, instead of admitting that there is an unconscious work, could we not admit that nothing at all occurs? Two chief hypotheses have been set forth.[5]

A. It has been supposed that an explanation for the new state of mind which makes illumination possible could lie in a *freshness* or lack of brain fatigue. This is what we can call the *rest-hypothesis*. Poincaré, though not adopting it, has thought of it but (see below) in a special case.

B. It can be admitted that an essential cause of illumination may be the *absence of interferences* which block progress during the preparation stage. "When, as must often happen, the thinker makes a false start, he slides insensibly into a groove and may not be able to escape at the moment. . . . Incubation would consist in getting rid of false leads and hampering assumptions so as to approach the problem with an 'open mind.' " We can call this the *forgetting-hypothesis*.

what they are—incurs, at least as much, the same objection of merely giving a name to our ignorance. That statement of Rossman, if it means anything, merely gives another name for the rest-hypothesis.

4 Exceptions seem to occur in cases such as Mozart's and, as Catherine Patrick observes in the work mentioned below in footnote 10, in A. E. Housman's (Cf. p. 37). For the reason given in the text, it seems to me certain that these exceptions must be apparent ones, due to a special rapidity of incubation.

5 See Woodworth's *Experimental Psychology*, p. 823.

Discussion of These Ideas. Helmholtz's testimony has been invoked in favor of the rest-hypothesis. Helmholtz says that "happy ideas" (his word for illumination) never come to him when his mind is fatigued or when he is seated at his work table;[6] and, mentioning his preparatory study of the question investigated, adds that "Then, after the fatigue resulting from this labor has passed away, there must come an hour of complete physical freshness before the good ideas arrive"—a statement which perhaps doubtfully supports the hypothesis in question, as illumination is not said to occur the moment mind is rested, but about an hour later.

Besides, the case of Helmholtz is not a universal one and there are observations to the contrary. Professor K. Friedrichs writes to me that "creative ideas" (if any) "come mostly of a sudden, frequently after great mental exertion, in a state of mental fatigue combined with physical relaxation"; and a similar statement has been given to me by a critic of art, Dr. Sterling, who has to solve problems concerning the authenticity of pictures. Dr. Sterling tells me he has noticed that, after long conscious effort, inspiration usually comes when he is fatigued, as though it were necessary for the conscious self to be weakened in order that unconscious ideas may break through.

[6] The question whether mathematicians usually stand or sit when working is one of those asked in the questionnaire of *L'Enseignement Mathématique*. Habits of that kind are certainly among those that vary most among individuals. Helmholtz's and Poincaré's statements seem to suggest that they often used to sit at a work table. I never do so, except when I am obliged to effectuate written calculations (for which I have a certain reluctance). Except in the night when I cannot sleep, I never find anything otherwise than by pacing up and down the room. I feel exactly like the character of Emile Augier who says: "Legs are the wheels of thought."

This instance shows, and we have to bear it in mind, that rules about such matters are not necessarily invariable ones. Processes may differ not only with individuals, but even in one and the same man. Indeed, the very observations of Poincaré show us three kinds of inventive work essentially different if considered from our standpoint, viz.,

a. fully conscious work.

b. illumination preceded by incubation.

c. the quite peculiar process of his first sleepless night.[7]

Moreover, we have said that Poincaré has thought of the rest-hypothesis. He has thought of it (without being inclined to adopt it even then) in connection with a special case, even different, as it seems, from the three mentioned above and which is quite similar to Helmholtz's description, viz., a first and unsuccessful work-period, a rest—a new half-hour of work (Helmholtz speaks of one hour) after which discovery comes. As he himself says, this could be explained by the rest-hypothesis, but with the same objection as in the case of Helmholtz.

Still other processes are possible. A very curious one is reported by the chemist J. Teeple[8] who, after half an hour, realized that he had been working on a question without being aware that he was doing so, and in such an abstracted state of mind that during that time he forgot that he had already taken a bath and was taking a second one: a special case of unconscious process, as the thinker was not con-

[7] Unhappily, Poincaré, when telling us that that night was not the only one when he has been able to watch the action of his subconscious self, does not enter into further particulars. More details would have been interesting about the first night in question.

[8] See Platt and Baker, *Journ. Chemical Educ.*, Vol. VIII (1931), pp. 1969-2002.

scious of his mental work while it was going on, but perceived it when it ended.

Thus there are several possibilities, and some of them might be explained by the rest or forgetting hypotheses. I willingly admit that a "fresh" or "open" mind—that is, forgetting of some unsuccessful attempts—can account for discovery when the latter is separated from the first conscious period by a long interval, say some months. I speak, in that case, of discovery, not of illumination, because this is not, properly speaking, illumination: the solution does not appear suddenly and unexpectedly, but is given by a new work.

Also, forgetting could, perhaps, as Professor Woodworth notices,[9] explain illuminations which would reveal solutions of an especially great simplicity, it happening that such may be at first overlooked. Any other ones, in the hypotheses we are dealing with, would require a new effort of the mind in a new condition (whether on account of rest or on account of forgetting previous ideas) to resume the subject. Such explanations are, therefore, to be rejected unhesitatingly in those cases of suddenness which are reported by Poincaré and confirmed by other authors. Poincaré was not working when he boarded the omnibus of Coutances: he was chatting with a companion; the idea passed through his mind for less than one second, just the time to put his foot on the step and enter the omnibus. It cannot even be said that the idea was simple enough not to require any work. Poincaré informs us that he had to work it out for verification on his return to Caen. Though not as strictly limited in time, other illuminations reported by

[9] See the above cited p. 823 of his *Experimental Psychology*.

Poincaré occur with the same suddenness and unprepared-
ness which exclude the proposed explanations.

If we admitted any one of them, illuminations ought to
come as a result of a new work of the same kind as the preliminary one, from which it could differ only by elimination
of the result—paradoxically, an exclusively harmful one
(be it fatigue or a misleading idea)—of that preliminary
work. Now, observation shows that the illumination process
is *not* of the same nature as the previous conscious work.
The latter is really work, implying a more or less severe
tenseness of mind and often multiplied attempts; the for- ·
mer occurs at once, without any perceptible effort.

Besides, if we should accept the forgetting hypothesis,
that is, that several previous and inappropriate ideas precede and for a while block the right one, we ought to be
aware of them (as these theories precisely claim to exclude
any role of the unconscious). On the contrary, most often,
instead of seeing several ways supposedly likely to lead to
the solution, we conceive no such ideas at all.

To sum it up, we see that such explanations as the rest or
the forgetting hypotheses can be admitted in some cases,
but that in other instances, especially typical illuminations
as noted by Poincaré and others, they are contradicted by
facts.[10]

[10] Catherine Patrick (*Archives of Psychology*, Vol. 26, 1935, No. 178)
has carried out an experimental study of poetical invention: she has
asked several persons—some being professional poets, others not—to
write a poem suggested by a picture shown them. Contrary to her
opinion, I cannot consider the process she observed as being comparable
to those we investigate. The time of the experiment—hardly more than
twenty minutes—shows that she deals with a quite different question;
and her so-called incubation, where subjects are required to relate aloud
the course of their thoughts during their attempt to do the required work,
has nothing to do with incubation as Helmholtz or Poincaré consider it,

Other Views on Illumination. An Intimation Stage. An objection of another kind, one less essential, has been raised[11] against Helmholtz's and Poincaré's descriptions of the phenomenon of illumination. Does not a part of it take place in what we have previously called the fringe-consciousness?

Now, fringe-consciousness and proper consciousness are so close to each other, exchanges between them are so continuous and so rapid, that it seems hardly possible to see how they divide their roles in that sudden lightninglike phenomenon of illumination. However, in consequence of what we shall find in Section VI, we shall be led to some probable views on that subject.

Another most curious circumstance has been noted. For some thinkers, while engaged in creative work, illumination may be preceded by a kind of warning by which they are made aware that something of that nature is imminent without knowing exactly what it will be. Wallas has given the name of "intimation" to that peculiar phenomenon. I never experienced any such sensation and Poincaré does not speak of it, which he certainly would have done if it had happened to him. An inquiry on that point among scientists would be useful.[11a]

A last objection against Poincaré's ideas has been raised by Wallas. This author admits that Poincaré may be right in saying "that without a rather high degree of this aesthetic instinct no man will ever be a great mathematical discoverer," but adds that "it is extremely unlikely that the

in which that course of thought, inasmuch as it refers to the research, may remain totally unknown to the subject.

[11] Graham Wallas, *The Art of Thought*, p. 96.

[11a] Later inquiry brought a few affirmative answers.

aesthetic instinct alone was the 'power' driving the 'machine' of his thought."

I can but reproduce textually that passage of Wallas,
because I hardly understand it. It seems to me to rest on
an evident confusion between two things which must be
distinguished[12] from each other: the "drive" (i.e., "what to
do") and the "mechanism"[13] ("how to do it"). We shall
speak of "drive" in Section IX (and again find that the
sense of beauty *is* the moving power): for the time being,
we deal with mechanism; and what that mechanism is, I can
hardly doubt. Wallas suspects Poincaré of thinking thus
because he was a friend of Boutroux, who was a friend of
William James, or because he was influenced by the ideas of
the "Mechanist" school. Not only is Poincaré's statement
the result of his own observations and not anybody else's
suggestions; but personally, I feel exactly as he does, not
because of having been a special friend of Boutroux or
William James, or having studied the Mechanist school
(which I have not) or any other one, but on account of my
own auto-observation—because the ideas chosen by my
unconscious are those which reach my consciousness, and I
see that they are those which agree with my aesthetic sense.

As a matter of fact, I consider that every mathematician,
if not every scientist, would agree to that opinion. I may
add that actually some of them, writing to me on the general subject of this work, spontaneously (i.e., without a
question from me on that special point) expressed themselves in the same sense, in the most positive way.

[12] See Woodworth's *Dynamic Psychology*.
[13] I am obliged to use almost simultaneously both words "mechanism"
and (see below) "mechanist," the meanings of which are quite different
and independent. I hope this will not make any confusion in the reader's
mind.

Further Theories on the Unconscious. Certainly, our above conclusions are, to a certain extent, surprising. They raised for Poincaré a disconcerting question. The unconscious is usually said to be automatic and, in a certain sense, it undoubtedly is so, as it is not subjected to our will, at least not to the direct action of our will, and even is subtracted from our knowledge. But now we find an opposite conclusion. The unconscious self "is not purely automatic; it is capable of discernment; it has tact, delicacy; it knows how to choose, to divine. What do I say? It knows better how to divine than the conscious self, since it succeeds where that has failed.

"In a word, is not the subliminal self superior to the conscious self?"[14]

Now, such an idea has been in favor among metaphysicians in recent times and even in more ancient ones. The very fact that unconsciousness, though manifesting itself from time to time, is not really known to us, has given it a mysterious character and, on account of that mysterious character, it has often been endowed with superior powers.[15] That unconsciousness may be something not exclusively originating in ourselves and even participating in Divinity seems already to have been admitted by Aristotle. In Leibniz's opinion, it sets the man in communication with the whole universe, in which nothing could occur without its repercussion in each of us; and something analogous is to

[14] Here Poincaré alludes to Emile Boutroux, whose influence on him certainly existed in this case.

[15] Similar cases obviously occur as concerns dreams, which, since the world exists, have been supposed to enjoy a kind of prophetic value. But it would be too disrespectful to compare metaphysical theories of the unconscious with the popular "Clue to Dreams" books.

be found in Schelling; again, Divinity is invoked by Fichte; etc.

Even more recently, a whole philosophical doctrine has been built on that principle in the first place by Myers, then by William James himself (although the great philosopher, in an earlier work, his *Principles of Psychology*, expresses himself, at times, as though doubting the very existence of unconsciousness). According to that doctrine, the unconscious would set man in connection with a world other than the one which is accessible to our senses and with some kinds of spiritual beings.

Meanwhile, unconsciousness appears to other authors as being the trace of prior existence; and others again suggest the possibility that it is due to the action of disembodied spirits.

Since celestial causes are thus set forth, we must not wonder too much at hearing that infernal ones can be invoked; and that is what has actually happened. An audacious philosopher, the German von Hartmann, considers the unconscious as a universal force, specifically an evil one, which influences things and beings in a constantly harmful way; and such is the pessimism generated in him by the fear of that terrible unconscious that he advises not individual suicide, which he considers as insufficient, but "cosmic suicide," hoping that powerful forces of destruction will be devised by mankind, enabling it to destroy at once the whole planet: a kind of foresight of what is taking place as these lines are written.

We have seen how some authors had a kind of fear of the unconscious and were even unwilling to admit its very existence. Perhaps this unwillingness is a kind of reaction against the flights of imagination which some others have indulged in about it. The same mysterious character imputed to it seems to have repelled some and overexcited others.

The question is whether there is any mystery, or more exactly, any special mystery. The true mystery lies in the existence of any thoughts, of any mental processes whatever, those mental processes being connected—in a way about which we hardly know anything more than mankind did thousands of years ago—with the functioning of some of our brain cells. The existence of several kinds of such processes is hardly more mysterious than the existence of one kind of them.

As to the unconscious mind being "superior" or "inferior" to the conscious one, I should deny any meaning to such a question and consider that no question of "superiority" or "inferiority" is a scientific one. When you ride a horse, is he inferior or superior to you? He is stronger than you are and can run more quickly than you can; however, you make him do what you want him to do. I do not know what would be meant by saying that oxygen is superior or inferior to hydrogen; nor is the right leg superior or inferior to the left one: they cooperate for walking. So do the conscious and the unconscious, a cooperation which we shall consider presently.

IV. THE PREPARATION STAGE.
LOGIC AND CHANCE

Throughout Conscious Work. Reviewing Poincaré's lecture, the literary critic Emile Faguet wrote: "A problem ... reveals itself suddenly when it is no longer investigated, probably because it is no longer investigated and when one only expects, for a short time, to rest and relax: a fact which would prove—lazy people, it is to be feared, might make ill use of it—that rest is the condition of work."

It would, of course, be very easy if, being told of the terms of a problem, we could simply think that it would be very nice to find it, then go to bed and find the solution ready on awakening the next morning. Indeed, we could think it to be perhaps too easy from the moral point of view.

As a matter of fact, things by no means behave that way. In the first place, it often happens that, in some of its parts, the work is perfectly conscious.[1] This has been the case for some parts of Poincaré's work itself, as has been shown in the beginning: for instance, in the step just after the initial one.

Very typical, from that point of view, is Newton's discovery of universal attraction. He is reported to have been asked how he had obtained it and to have answered, "By constantly thinking it over"; but we do not need that anecdote, which may not be authentic, to understand that his

[1] However, the word "conscious" ought not, perhaps, to be understood in too strict a sense. A more attentive analysis will show us (see Section VI) a cooperation between perfect consciousness and that superficial subconscious or "fringe-consciousness" we spoke of in Section II.

discovery was a work of high and inflexible logic, the main and essential idea, i.e., that the moon must really fall toward the earth, being a necessary and unavoidable consequence of the fact that any material body (be it an apple or not) does so. A tenacious continuity of attention, "a consented, a voluntary faithfulness to an idea"[2] was necessary for that.

Must we, then, agree with Buffon's thesis that genius may often be nothing else than a long patience? This idea is obviously contrary to all that we have noticed so far. I confess that I cannot share the admiration for it, nor even approve of it. In Newton's case, one can certainly see, from the beginning, a continuous course of thought constantly directed toward its goal. But this process was started by the initial recognition that the subject was worthy of this continuity of attention, of the consented and voluntary faithfulness we have just spoken of. This is again an inspiration, a choice; only, this takes place in the conscious will.

Conscious Work as Preparatory. Let us now consider the opposite case, the unexpected inspirations which repeatedly illuminated Poincaré's mind. We have acquired the notion that they are the consequence of a more or less intense and lengthy unconscious work. But is that unconscious work itself an effect without a cause? We should be utterly mistaken in thinking so; we have only to come back to Poincaré's report to be led to the contrary conclusion. His first inspiration on getting into the car at Coutances follows a preliminary period of deliberate labor; and after that, we see him studying arithmetical questions "apparently without much success" and finally, "disgusted with his failure";

---

[2] Delacroix, *L'Invention et le Génie*.

upon which new fruitful steps reveal themselves to him. Then he makes a systematic attack upon the chief remaining question, "carrying all the outworks, one after the other. There was one, however, that still held out, whose fall would involve that of the whole place. But all my efforts only served at first the better to show me the difficulty, which indeed was something." And he again notices that all this work was perfectly conscious.

Only then, and after having been compelled even to set it aside for a while, the solution of the difficulty suddenly appeared.

In all these successive steps, as we see, "sudden inspirations (and the examples already cited sufficiently prove this), never happen except after some days of voluntary effort which has appeared absolutely fruitless and whence nothing good seems to have come, where the way taken seems totally astray. These efforts then have not been as sterile as one thinks. They have set going the unconscious machine and without them it would not have moved and would have produced nothing."

Helmholtz had similarly observed that what we have called incubation and illumination must be preceded by this stage of *preparation*. Its existence has been, after Helmholtz and Poincaré, recognized by psychologists as a general fact, and probably it exists even when it is not apparent, as in the case of Mozart (who does not mention incubation either).

It is not useless to notice that independently of the reasons we have already given, this, by itself, is sufficient to settle the question whether discovery is a matter of pure chance. Discovery cannot be produced only by chance, although chance is to some extent involved therein, any more than does the inevitable role of chance in artillery dispense with the necessity for the gunner to take aim, and to aim very precisely. Discovery necessarily depends on preliminary and more or less intense action of the conscious.

Not only does this answer the question of the chance-hypothesis, but at the same time it prevents us from admitting the other hypotheses which we have examined in the preceding section. It ought, indeed, to be noticed that the rest and forgetting hypotheses have one feature in common; whether it be in one or in the other of them, the preparatory work, if not bringing directly the solution by itself, is assumed to be completely useless and even harmful. Then, discovery would happen just as if there had been no preparation work at all; that is, we should be again compelled to go back to the inadmissible hypothesis of pure chance.

Poincaré's View on the Mode of Action of Preparatory Work. Having recognized this, we cannot any longer think of the conscious as being subordinated to the unconscious. On the contrary, it starts its action and defines, to a greater or lesser extent, the general direction in which that unconscious has to work.

To illustrate that directing action, Poincaré uses a striking and remarkably fruitful comparison. He imagines that the ideas which are the future elements of our combinations are "something like the hooked atoms of Epicurus. During the complete repose of the mind, these atoms are motionless; they are, so to speak, hooked to the wall; so this complete rest may be indefinitely prolonged without the atoms meeting, and consequently without any combination between them." The act of studying a question consists of mobilizing ideas, not just any ones, but those from which we might reasonably expect the desired solution. It may happen that that work has no immediate result. "We think we have done no good, because we have moved these elements a thousand different ways in seeking to assemble them and have found no satisfactory aggregate." But, as a matter of fact, it seems as though these atoms are thus launched, so to speak, like so many projectiles and flash in various directions through space. "After this shaking-up imposed upon them by our will, these atoms do not return to their primitive rest. They freely continue their dance."

Consequences can now be foreseen. "The mobilized atoms undergo impacts which make them enter into combinations among themselves or with other atoms at rest, which they struck against in their course." In those new combinations, in those indirect results of the original conscious work, lie the possibilities of apparently spontaneous inspiration.

Logic and Chance. Though Poincaré presents that comparison as a very rough one and it could hardly avoid being such, it proves, as a matter of fact, to be highly instructive.

We shall now see that, by pursuing it, other points can be elucidated. Let us consider, from that point of view, the question of logic and chance in discovery, on which authors are most divided. Several of them, though not as extreme as we have seen to be the case with Nicolle, insist on the importance of chance, while others emphasize the preeminence of logic. Among the two psychologists whom we mentioned in the beginning, Paulhan belongs to the latter school, while Souriau represents the former. It seems to me, in accordance with my personal introspection, that we can get a good understanding of that question by using Poincaré's comparison of projected atoms: a comparison which I shall complete by assimilating that projection with that which is produced by a hunting cartridge. It is well known that good hunting cartridges are those which have a proper scattering. If this scattering is too wide, it is useless to aim; but if it is too narrow, you have too many chances to miss your game by a line. I see quite similar circumstances in our subject. Again comparing ideas to Poincaré's atoms, it may happen that the mind projects them, exactly or almost exactly, in certain determinate directions. Doing so has this advantage that the proportion of useful meetings between them happens to be relatively great compared to the sterile ones; but we may fear lest these meetings be insufficiently different from each other. On the contrary, it may happen that the atoms are launched in a rather disorderly manner. If so, most of the meetings will be uninteresting ones; but on the other hand, as in a kind of lottery, that disorder can be highly valuable, because the few meetings which are useful, being of an exceptional nature and between seemingly very remote ideas, will probably be the most important ones.

This is what Souriau expresses by the quite striking phrase: "In order to invent, one must think aside";[3] and, even in mathematics—though, in that realm, its meaning is rather different from what it is in experimental sciences—we can remember Claude Bernard's statement, "Those who have an excessive faith in their ideas are not well fitted to make discoveries."

Errors and Failures. The reason for the difference between the meanings of Claude Bernard's sentence in mathematics and in experimental sciences is that, in the latter case, too stubbornly following an idea once conceived may lead to errors: that is, to inaccurate conclusions.

---

[3] "Pour inventer, il faut penser à côté."

On the contrary, in our domain, we do not need to ponder on errors. Good mathematicians, when they make them, which is not infrequent, soon perceive and correct them. As for me (and mine is the case of many mathematicians), I make many more of them than my students do; only I always correct them so that no trace of them remains in the final result. The reason for that is that whenever an error has been made, insight—that same scientific sensibility we have spoken of—warns me that my calculations do not look as they ought to.

There are, however, celebrated exceptions concerning some delicate points of reasoning; those may sometimes prove more fruitful than accurate results, as has been an insufficient proof of Riemann for "Dirichlet's principle."

But, in both domains, the mathematical and the experimental, the fact of not sufficiently "thinking aside" is a most ordinary cause of failure—i.e., the lack of success in finding a solution which may appear to better inspired thinkers—a circumstance which is at least as interesting as discovery for psychology.

This, especially, often explains the failures which may be called "paradoxical," viz., the failure of a research scholar to perceive an important immediate consequence of his own conclusions.

Of course, we must insist on speaking of *immediate* consequences. When the discoverer of a certain fact hears that another scholar has found a notable consequence of it, if this improvement has required some effort, the former will consider it not a failure but a success: he has the right to claim his part in the new discovery.

Such paradoxical failures are reported by Claparède in the lecture referred to (p. viii) and they are, in my opinion, explained as we have just said. The most striking instance which he gives, concerns the invention of the ophthalmoscope. The physiologist Brücke had investigated the means of illuminating the back part of the eye and succeeded in doing so; but it was Helmholtz who, while preparing a lecture on that result of Brücke, conceived the idea that optical images could be generated by the rays thus reflected by the retina: an almost obvious idea, which as it seems, Brücke could hardly have overlooked. In that case, most evidently—at least to me—Brücke's mind was too narrowly directed toward his problem.

Similarly, as Claparède also reports, de la Rive failed to invent the galvanoplastic method; Freud missed finding the application of cocaine to the surgery of the eye.

Personal Instances. Every scientist can probably record similar failures. In my own case, I have several times happened to overlook results which ought to have struck me blind, as being immediate consequences of other ones which I had obtained. Most of these failures proceed from the cause which we have just mentioned, viz., from attention too narrowly directed.

The first instance I remember in my life had to do with a formula which I obtained at the very beginning of my research work. I decided not to publish it and to wait till I could deduce some significant consequences from it. At that time, all my thoughts, like many other analysts', were concentrated on one question, the proof of the celebrated "Picard's theorem." Now, my formula most obviously gave one of the chief results which I found four years later by a much more complicated way: a thing which I was never aware of until years after, when Jensen published that formula and noted, as an evident consequence, the re-

sults which, happily for my self-esteem, I had obtained
in the meanwhile. It is clear that, in 1888, I had thought
too exclusively of Picard's theorem.

My next work was my thesis. Two theorems, important
to the subject,[4] were such obvious and immediate consequences of the ideas contained therein that, years later,
other authors imputed them to me, and I was obliged to
confess that, evident as they were, I had not perceived
them.

Some years later, I was interested in generalizing to
hyperspaces the classic notion of curvature of surfaces. I
had to deal with Riemann's notion of curvature in hyperspaces, which is the generalization of the more elementary
notion of the curvature of a surface in ordinary space.
What interested me was to obtain that Riemann curvature
as the curvature of a certain surface S, drawn in the considered hyperspace, the shape of S being chosen in order
to reduce the curvature to a minimum. I succeeded in showing that the minimum thus obtained was precisely Riemann's expression; only, thinking of that question, I
neglected to take into consideration the circumstances under which the minimum is reached, i.e., the proper way of
constructing S in order to reach the minimum. Now, investigating that would have led me to the principle of the
so-called "Absolute Differential Calculus," the discovery
of which belongs to Ricci and Levi Civita.

Absolute differential calculus is closely connected with
the theory of relativity; and in this connection, I must con-

[4] For technicians: "If the coefficients of a Maclaurin series are real
positive numbers, the radius of convergence being R, x = R must be a
singular point"; "A Maclaurin series with a finite radius of convergence
generally admits its whole circle of convergence as an essentially singular
line."

fess that, having observed that the equation of propagation of light is invariant under a set of transformations (what is now known as Lorentz's group) by which space and time are combined together, I added that "such transformations are obviously devoid of physical meaning." Now, these transformations, supposedly without any physical meaning, are the base of Einstein's theory.

To continue about my failures, I shall mention one which I particularly regret. It concerns the celebrated Dirichlet problem which I, for years, tried to solve in the same initial direction as Fredholm did, i.e., by reconducting it to a system of an infinite number of equations of the first degree in an infinite number of unknowns. But physical interpretation, which is in general a very sure guide and had been most often such for me, misled me in that case. It suggested an attempt to solve the problem by a "potential of simple layer"—in that question, a blind alley—while the solution was to be looked for in the introduction of a "potential of a double layer." This shows how justified Claude Bernard is in the above-mentioned sentence, and that one ought not to follow too stubbornly a determinate principle, however justifiable and fruitful in general.

In all these examples, as we see, the reason for the failures was basically the same. But the opposite case occurred when I overlooked the fact that a problem in "inversive geometry" could be indeterminate—a fact which leads to the beautiful properties discovered by André Bloch. It is not, this time, a consequence of having too strictly followed my original direction, which would precisely have led me to discuss more thoroughly the problem which I had solved, and therefore, to notice the possibility of indetermination.

That case is exactly contrary to the preceding ones. I was unsufficiently faithful to my main idea.

I must close the enumeration of these failures with one which I can hardly explain: having found, for constructing conditions of possibility for a problem in partial differential equations,[5] a method which gives the result in a very complicated and intricate form, how did I fail to notice, in my own calculations, a feature which enlightens the whole problem, and leave that discovery to happier and better inspired successors? That is what is difficult for me to conceive.

The Case of Pascal. It is probable that many scholars, if not all of them, can remember similar experiences. It is a comforting thing to think that the same may happen to some of the greatest ones.

In his *Art de Persuader*, Pascal has stated a principle which is fundamental for method not only in mathematics, but in any deductive subject or any matter of reasoning, viz.:

"One must substitute definitions instead of the defined."

On the other hand, in another place, he points out the obvious fact that, for the same reason that it is not possible to prove everything, it is also impossible to define everything. There are primitive ideas which it is not possible to define.

If he had only thought of juxtaposing these two statements, he would have found himself before a great problem of logic which not only enables us to understand the true

[5] For technicians: see pp. 257-260 of my Yale *Lectures on Cauchy's Problem*; pp. 351-355 of the French edition. The improved answer is given in Hilbert-Courant's *Methoden der Mathematischen Physik* (pp. 425-430), following works of John and Asgueiersson.

meaning of the celebrated Euclid postulate, but, more generally, has produced a profound revolution which, as we see it, might have taken place three centuries earlier.

However, he did not connect both ideas. Whether the reason for this was that his thoughts were too intensely directed toward theological consequences, as a friend of mine suggested to me, is a question which it would be difficult to elucidate.[6]

Attempts to Govern our Unconscious. Such instances show us that, in research, it may be detrimental to scatter our attention too much, while overstraining it too strongly in one particular direction may also be harmful to discovery.

What should we do in order to avoid these opposite objections?

Of course, there is the obvious influence of the way in which we direct our preparation work which gives the impulse to the unconscious work: and in fact, especially with reference to Poincaré's conception, this can be considered as a way to educate our unconscious. The formula of Souriau, "To invent, one must think aside," is to be understood in that sense.

But this is not yet completely satisfactory: in this way we shall think of expected directions for "aside" thoughts, but not of those unexpected and all the more interesting for this very reason. We must notice, in that direction, that it is important for him who wants to discover not to confine himself to one chapter of science, but to keep in touch with various others.

Could we find other means of influencing our unconscious? That would be of great importance, in fact not only for invention but also for the whole conduct of life and es-

6 See Appendix III.

pecially for education. The study of that question, which
deserves to be pursued, has been undertaken at least in one
periodical, *La Psychologie et la Vie*; a whole fascicle was
devoted to it by that review in 1932, with contributions
of several authors. Particularly, Dwelshauvers suggests an
analysis of the conditions of the phenomenon, such as the
time of the day at which it takes place, how much time
elapses between voluntary preparation and solution;
whether such incubation lasts for hours or for days,
whether its duration is in proportion to the difficulty of the
question, etc.

Pending the results of such studies, one rule proves evidently useful: that is, after working on a subject and seeing no further advance seems possible, to drop it and try
something else, but to do so provisionally, intending to resume it after an interval of some months. This is useful
advice for every student who is beginning research work.

There is another direction in which that education of the
unconscious could be pursued, though I cannot undertake
to speak of it. Indeed, as Dr. de Saussure suggested to me,
very powerful means for that purpose may be supplied by
the methods of psychoanalysis.

V. THE LATER CONSCIOUS WORK

The Fourth Stage. We have now become acquainted with the three stages in invention which Helmholtz and Poincaré have taught us to distinguish: preparation, incubation and illumination. But Poincaré shows the necessity and importance of a fourth and final one, which again occurs in consciousness. This new intervention of consciousness, after the unconscious work, is necessary not only for the obvious purpose of expressing the results by language or writing, but at least for three other reasons which are, however, closely dependent on each other:

(1) To Verify Them. The feeling of absolute certitude which accompanies the inspiration generally corresponds to reality; but it may happen that it has deceived us.[1] Whether such has been the case or not must be ascertained by our properly so-called reason, a task which belongs to our conscious self.

(2) To "Precise" Them. That is, to state them precisely. It never happens, as Poincaré observes, that the unconscious work gives us the results of a somewhat long calculation already solved in its entirety. If we should, as concerns the unconscious, retain the original idea which is suggested by the quality "automatic" imputed to it, we should suppose that, thinking of an algebraic calculation before falling asleep, we might hope to find its result ready made upon our awakening; but nothing of the sort ever happens, and indeed we begin to understand that automa-

[1] Poincaré notices that this happens to him especially in regard to ideas coming to him in the morning or evening, or in bed while in a semihypnagogic state.

tism of the unconscious must not be understood in that
way. On the contrary, effective calculations which require
discipline, attention and volition, and, therefore, consciousness, depend on the second period of conscious work which
follows the inspiration.

Thus, we come to the paradoxical-looking conclusion—
to which, besides, we shall have to bring a correction as we
already have done in Newton's case—that this intervention
of our will, i.e., of one of the highest faculties of our soul,
happens in a rather mechanical part of the work, where it
is in some way subordinated to the unconscious, though
supervising it. The second operation is inseparable from
the first, from verification. The conscious mind performs
them both at the same time.

A Statement by Paul Valéry. What we just met with in
the domain of mathematical research, especially that co-
ordination of the "precising" work to the original inspiration, is once more in agreement with what Paul Valéry says
on quite a different kind of invention, except that the very
description of Paul Valéry suggests that facts may be even
more complicated or delicate than he himself or Poincaré
saw them, and would deserve a more thorough study. Paul
Valéry says, in the passage[2] of which we have already
quoted the beginning (see Section I, p. 17) :

"There is the period of dark-room. There must be no excessive zeal at this moment, or you would spoil your plate.
You must have your reagents, you must work as your own
employee, your own foreman. The master has provided the
spark, it is your job to make something of it. A very curious thing is the disappointment that may follow. There are
misleading gleams of light; when the foreman comes to the

[2] *Bulletin Soc. Philosophie,* Vol. 28 (1928), p. 16.

result, he perceives that there is no authentic product, that it would have been good *if* it had been true. Sometimes a series of judgments intervene which cancel each other out. A kind of irritation follows; you say yourself you will never succeed in recording what appears before you."

This "precising" state in invention is again quite a general one, and even the most spontaneous creators experience it. The same Lamartine whom we have seen to answer so rapidly, unhesitatingly and as though almost unwillingly when asked for a couple of verses, is reported by his biographers to have repeatedly and indefatigably corrected his work, as appears from his manuscripts.

Numerical Calculators. The process seems to be slightly different, on one point, in a case which one is often tempted to mix with that of mathematicians: I mean those prodigious calculators—frequently quite uneducated men—who can very rapidly make very complicated numerical calculations, such as multiplications of numbers in ten or more figures, who will want only one instant of reflection to tell you how many minutes or seconds have elapsed since the beginning of our era.

Such a talent is, in reality, distinct from mathematical ability. Very few known mathematicians are said to have possessed it: one knows the case of Gauss and Ampère and also in the seventeenth century, Wallis. Poincaré confesses that he is a rather poor numerical calculator, and so am I.

Exceptional calculators often present remarkable psychological peculiarities.[3] The one I want to mention as belonging to our subject is that, contrary to what we just heard from Poincaré, it happens that calculation results,

[3] We mention the very curious one that, in several of them, that ability has been temporary and disappeared after some years.

or at least partial ones, appear to them without willful effort and by inspiration elaborated in their unconscious.

Perhaps the most outspoken testimony is afforded by a letter written to Möbius[4] by the calculator Ferrol: "If I was asked any question, rather a difficult one by itself, the result immediately proceeded from my sensibility without my knowing at the first moment how I had obtained it; starting from the result, I then sought the way to be followed for this purpose. That intuitive conception which, curiously enough, has never been shaken by an error, has developed more and more as needs increased. Even now, I have often the sensation of somebody beside me whispering the right way to find the desired result; it concerns some ways where few people have entered before me and which I should certainly not have found if I had sought for them by myself.

"It often seems to me, especially when I am alone, that I find myself in another world. Ideas of numbers seem to live. Suddenly, questions of any kind rise before my eyes with their answers."

It must be added that Ferrol was attracted not only by numerical calculations, but also and even more strongly by algebraic ones. It is the more striking that, also in that case, he brings calculations to an effective end in an unconscious way.[5]

[4] See *Die Anlage für Mathematik*, pp. 74-76.

[5] Unconscious interventions in numerical calculations are also reported by Scripture, *American Journal of Psych.*, Vol. IV (1891). See also Binet, *Psychologie des Grands Calculateurs et Joueurs d'Echecs*. However, these statements are not as positive and precise as Ferrol's, and confusion would be possible between partial results unconsciously obtained and results known in advance by heart.

Appreciation of One's Own Work. Once we have obtained our result, what do we think of it?

Very often research which has deeply interested me while I was investigating it loses its interest for me just after I have the solution, unhappily at a time which coincides with the period when I have to record it. After a while, say a couple of months, I come to a more just appreciation of it.

Paul Valéry was asked the same question about his feeling toward his own work after its completion at a meeting of the Société de Philosophie in Paris; he answered: "It always turns out badly; *Je divorce*"; and he already gave an indication in the same sense when describing the invention process, as we have seen.

(3) The Continuation of the Work. Relay-Results. The double operation of verifying and "precising" the result assumes another meaning when, as happens most frequently, we regard it not as the end of the research, but as one stage of it—we have met with such successive stages in Poincaré's report—so that we think of *utilizing* it.

Such a utilization not only requires that the result be verified, but that it be "precised." Indeed, since we know that our unconscious work, showing us the way to obtain the result, does not offer it in its precise form, it may happen, and it actually happens in many cases, that some features in that precise form, which we could not fully foresee, wield a capital and even total influence on the continuation of the thought.

Such has already been the case with Poincaré's initial stage (though not for the following ones). We hear from him that he originally supposed that the functions which he has called fuchsian could *not* exist, and it was only the fact of having discovered, in his sleepless night, the opposite conclusion which gave his following thoughts the course they took.

That each planet moves around the sun as being attracted by it with a force proportional to the inverse square of a distance, was found by Newton to be the interpretation of the first two laws of Kepler. But there is a coefficient of proportionality—the ratio between the force of attraction and the inverse square of the distance, which ratio does not vary during the motion—and the meaning of that coefficient is to be deduced from the third law of Kepler, which concerns the comparison between the motions of different planets. The conclusion is that this coefficient is the same for all of them. All planets obey the *same* law of attraction; that conclusion does not arise from the general and synthetic view of the question, but from a precise and careful calculation. One may doubt whether Newton can have reached that last conclusion otherwise than by calculating pen in hand. Now, if the result of those calculations had been a different one, the last step of the discovery, that of identifying the force which keeps the moon revolving around the earth with the one which makes a heavy body (an apple, if we believe the legend) fall down, would not have existed.

Perhaps it is imprudent to imagine how Newton's mind functioned; but it may be noticed that the identification which he viewed required not only an algebraic but even a numerical verification, using the observed values of the magnitudes involved in the formulae (a verification which even, as is well known, was temporarily believed by Newton to be wrong), and if, strictly speaking, there could remain a doubt as to Newton's example, others are completely beyond doubt. For instance, it is certain that Georg Cantor could not have foreseen a result of which he himself says "I see it, but I do not believe it."

In any case, moreover, the continuation of the work, just as was the case for its beginning, requires the preparation work we have spoken of. After a first stage of research has been brought to an end, the following one requires a new impulse, which can be originated and directed only when our consciousness takes account of the first *precise* result.

To take a rather familiar example, everybody understands that, intersecting two parallel straight lines by two other parallel ones, the segments thus determined are equal two by two; everybody knows that, consciously or not. But as long as it is not consciously enunciated, none of its consequences, such as similitude, can be deduced.

One of the possible cases is that the new part of the research be one which is to be carried out by exclusively conscious work, as Poincaré reports (more exactly, as I should say, by conscious work with the cooperation of fringe-consciousness) ; or even, as in Newton's example, one which deserves and requires a systematic and exhaustive work of that kind. To recognize such cases is again a task of our volition and the precise result is essential for that.

To sum up, every stage of the research has to be, so to speak, articulated to the following one by a result in a precise form, which I should propose to call a *relay-result* (or a *relay-formula* if it is a formula, as in Newton's interpretation of Kepler's third law). When reaching such a joining, somewhat analogous to railroad bifurcations, the new direction in which further research will follow must be decided, so that they clearly illustrate the directing action of that conscious ego which we were tempted to consider as "inferior" to unconsciousness.

The above remarks may seem to a certain extent obvious, if not childish; but it is not useless to notice that, besides the processes in the mind of any individual researchmen, they help us to understand the structure of mathematical science in general. Its improvement would have been impossible not only without verification of the results, but especially without the systematic use of what we have just called relay-results, which are very often intensely and exhaustively utilized as much as possible to the extreme end of their consequences. Such is, for instance, the role of the simple and classic fact that cutting a triangle by a parallel to one of its sides, we obtain another triangle similar to the former: a self-evident fact, but one which needed to be precisely enunciated in order to yield the long series of properties which proceed from it.

Incubation and Relay-results. The above has a connection with what we said in Section III. There is undoubtedly (at least in my own case) a process—different from those mentioned in Section III—which takes place during incubation, when a relay-result occurs. It most often happens that such a result needs to be digested, or to say it differently, to be classed in our fringe-consciousness, so as to be "ready for use." Then it can easily and rapidly find its place in the synthetic scheme of the deduction (see Section VI). That such a process is unconscious and that it corresponds to an incubation stage cannot be denied. Having reached an intermediate result which seems to be useful for further investigation, in many cases I deliberately leave the whole work sleeping till the following day, when I find it "ready for use."

VI. DISCOVERY AS A SYNTHESIS.
THE HELP OF SIGNS

Synthesis in Discovery. Souriau, in his *Théorie de l'Invention*, writes, "Does the algebraist know what becomes of his ideas when he introduces them, in the form of signs, into his formulae? Does he follow them throughout every stage of the operations which he performs? Undoubtedly not: he immediately loses sight of them. His only concern is to put in order and to combine, according to known rules, the signs which he has before him; and he accepts with a full confidence the result thus obtained."

We have said that this author hardly seems to have gathered information from professional men. Probably, if he had, he would not have expressed himself in that way. One cannot say, however, that his statement is completely false. It can be admitted to be true, roughly speaking, as far as concerns the final phase of verifying and "precising" already mentioned in the preceding section; but, even then, things do not occur as he states. The mathematician does not so blindly confide in the results of the rules which he uses. He knows that faults of calculation are possible and even not infrequent; if the purpose of the calculation is to verify a result which unconscious or subconscious inspiration has foreseen and if this verification fails it is by no means impossible that the calculation be at first false and the inspiration be right.

If applied not to that final phase but to the total research work, the behavior which Souriau describes is that of the pupil, and even of the rather bad pupil; our efforts aim to have him change it. The true process of thought in building up a mathematical argument is certainly rather to be compared with the process we mentioned in Section II, I mean the act of recognizing a person. An intermediate case which illustrates the analogy between the two processes is afforded by psychological studies on chess players, some of whom, as is well known, can play ten or twelve games simultaneously without seeing the chess boards. Inquiries were started, especially by Alfred Binet, in order to understand how this was possible: their results[1] may be summed up by saying that for many of these players, each game has, so to say, a kind of physiognomy, which allows him to think of it as a unique thing, however complicated it may be, just as we see the face of a man.

Now, such a phenomenon necessarily occurs in invention of any kind. We saw it mentioned in Mozart's letter (see Section I); similar statements are issued by artists like Ingres or Rodin (quoted by Delacroix, *L'Invention et le Génie*, p. 459). Only, while the happily gifted Mozart does not seem to have needed any effort in order to see the unity of his work, Rodin writes, "Till the end of his task, it is necessary for him [the sculptor] to maintain energetically, in the full light of his consciousness, his global idea, so as to reconduct unceasingly to it and closely connect with it the smallest details of his work. And this cannot be done without a very severe strain of thought."

Similarly, any mathematical argument, however complicated, must appear to me as a unique thing. I do not feel that I have understood it as long as I do not succeed in grasping it in one global idea and, unhappily, as with

[1] See, e.g., Binet's article in the *Revue des Deux Mondes*, Series 3, Vol. 117 (May-June, 1893), pp. 826-859, especially Section IV.

Rodin, this often requires a more or less painful exertion of thought.

The Use of Signs. Let us now examine a question which, as I intend to show below, is connected with the preceding one: the help which is afforded to thought by concrete representations. Such an investigation, belonging to the field of direct introspection, is possible thanks only to that fringe-consciousness which we mentioned at the end of Section II. However, we shall see that its chief results most probably also subsist in the deeper unconscious, though the latter is not directly known to us.

Words and Wordless Thought. The most classic kind of signs spoken of as cooperating with thought consists of words. Here we face a curious question on which quite divergent opinions are held.

I had a first hint of this when I read in *Le Temps* (1911): "The idea cannot be conceived otherwise than through the word and only exists by the word."[2] My feeling was that the ideas of the man who wrote that were of a poor quality.

But it was even more surprising for me to see such a man as Max Müller, the celebrated philologist and orientalist, maintain[3] that no thought is possible without words[4] and even write this sentence, fully unintelligible to me: "How do we know that there is a sky and that it is blue?

[2] I have also seen the following topic (a deplorable subject, as far as I can judge) proposed for an examination—an elementary one, the "baccalauréat"—in philosophy in Paris: "To show that language is as necessary for us to think as it is to communicate our thoughts."

[3] *Three Introductory Lectures on the Science of Thought*, delivered in London in 1887: Chicago, 1888; and also his more extensive work, *The Science of Thought*, published the same year.

[4] It is quite possible that M. Müller's unlimited confidence in words may be due to the linguistic work of his whole life.

Should we know of a sky if we had no name for it?", admitting not only, with Herder, that "without language, man could never have come to his reason," but also adding that, without language, man could never have come even to his senses. Are animals, which do not speak, devoid of senses?

That statement of Max Müller is the more curious because he claims to find in the fact that thought is impossible without words an argument against every evolutionary theory, a proof that man cannot be descended from any animal species. The deduction, even admitting the premise, is contestable. But it could more legitimately be reversed against Max Müller's thesis if we take into account, for instance, Köhler's *Mentality of Apes*[5] and the actions of his chimpanzees, which do imply reasoning.

Max Müller gives a historical review, which we shall reproduce in its essential parts, of opinions expressed on the question of words in thought: a review which is not devoid of interest, first in itself, next, because of the standpoint of Max Müller toward it. We hear, in the first place, that the Greeks originally used one and the same word, "logos," to denote language and thought and only later on were led to distinguish both meanings by epithets—on which, of course, the author declares them better inspired in the former case than in the latter.

Medieval scholastics, by a similitude which perhaps lies in the nature of things, agree with the beginning of Greek philosophy. Abelard, in the twelfth century, said that "Language is generated by the intellect and generates intellect." An analogous statement is to be found in a more

[5] N.Y. 1923. See, e.g., the experiment of the "jointed stick," p. 132.

modern philosopher, Hobbes (who, generally, keeps in sympathy with the scholastics).

But, as a rule, ideas took a different course, on that subject as on many others, with the stream of thought initiated by Descartes. There is only one period in Germany, around 1800 (Humboldt, Schelling, Hegel, Herder) when philosophical minds were near to "truth," that is, to Max Müller's opinion. Hegel summarily says, "We think in nouns," as if nobody had ever doubted it.

But the other great philosophers of modern times are not so sure of the identity of language and reason. Precisely, the greatest of them—be it Locke, Leibniz or even Kant or Schopenhauer, or, more recently, John Stuart Mill—agree in a methodic doubt. Not that Leibniz does not think in words, but he does not recognize that without openly regretting it.[6] One philosopher, Berkeley, is absolutely categorical—but in the opposite direction. He is convinced that words are the great impediment to thought.

Max Müller's passionate view of the subject leads him to qualify as "lack of courage" that general attitude of modern thinkers, which everybody else would call scientific prudence, as though no sincere opinion other than his own might exist.

Whether he admits it or not, it does exist. Immediately after the *Lectures on Science of Thought* were delivered, contradictions arose; indeed they came from most various parts.[7] Above all, there came the authorized voice of another first-rank scholar, Francis Galton, the great ge-

[6] *Dialogue on the Connection Between Things and Words*: "It troubles me greatly [Hoc unum me male habet] to find that I can never acknowledge, discover or prove any truth except by using in my mind words or other things."

[7] See the exchange of letters at the end of the *Introductory Lectures*.

neticist, who, moreover, after having begun as an explorer, has done important work in psychological matters. The latter's great habit of introspection allows him to assert that his mind does not behave at all in the way supposed by Max Müller to be the only possible one. Whether he is playing billiards and calculating the course of his ball or investigating higher and more abstract questions, his thought is never accompanied by words.

Galton adds that he sometimes happens, while engaged in thinking, to catch an accompaniment of *nonsense* words, just "as the notes of a song might accompany thought." Of course, nonsense words are something quite different from real words; we shall see later to what kind of images they may be reasonably compared.

That disposition of mind in Galton is not devoid of inconvenience for him. "It is," he says, "a serious drawback to me in writing, and still more in explaining myself, that I do not so easily think in words as otherwise. It often happens that after being hard at work, and having arrived at results that are perfectly clear and satisfactory to myself, when I try to express them in language I feel that I must begin by putting myself upon quite another intellectual plane. I have to translate my thoughts into a language that does not run very evenly with them. I therefore waste a vast deal of time in seeking for appropriate words and phrases, and am conscious, when required to speak on a sudden, of being often very obscure through mere verbal maladroitness, and not through want of clearness of perception. That is one of the small annoyances of my life."

I have wanted to reproduce at length that statement of Galton, because in his case I exactly recognize mine, including the rather regrettable consequence which I experience just as he does.

The fact that it is impossible for Max Müller to recall lightning without thinking of its name does not mean that "we" are unable to do so. As for myself, if I remember lightning, I see in my mind the flash of light which I have admired several times, and I should need an instant of reflection—a short one, of course, but certainly an instant— if I should wish the corresponding word to recur to me. Just as for Galton, such a translation from thought to language always requires on my part a more or less difficult effort. Whether the verses of Boileau

"Ce qui se conçoit bien s'énonce clairement
Et les mots pour le dire arrivent aisément,"

are justified or not concerning other people, it is certain that they are not true for me. I have a tangible proof of that—an "objective" one, I could say—in the fact that it is difficult for me to deliver a lecture on anything but mathematical subjects without having written down practically every part of it, the only means of avoiding constant and painful hesitation in the expression of thought which is very clear in my mind.

Galton legitimately points out how strange it is that Max Müller has utterly failed to understand that other people's minds may be different from his own: a most common error, but one which it is surprising to find among men accustomed to psychological studies. Differences between minds being, on the contrary, undeniable according to what we have just found, the question ought to be settled not by polemics but by inquiries relating to every human race and every class of men and, if possible (we shall see that there may be some difficulty in this), not only among intellectual people. Galton, inquiring, as he says, as much as occasion has allowed him, finds a certain percentage, though a minor one, of persons whose thought is habitually carried on without the use of mental or spoken words. One may wonder that a man as well acquainted with statistical operations as Galton does not give a precise percentage; a possible reason for that will appear below.[8]

Mental Pictures in Usual Thought. Thought can be accompanied by concrete representations other than words. Aristotle admitted that we cannot think without images. Taine's well-known work *On Intelligence* is chiefly devoted to the importance, in the constitution of ideas, of images, which he defines, at the beginning of his Volume II, as recurring, surviving and spontaneously resurging sensations. However, he is now believed to have exaggerated that importance and described it as a too exclusive one.

At about the same time, Alfred Binet was making an important improvement in the study of that question by attacking it in the experimental way.[9] He investigated some twenty persons, but chiefly two young girls (aged thirteen and fourteen) in his own family, whose valuable help in somewhat delicate psychological researches, at such a youthful age, is a very remarkable thing. He submits them sometimes to pure experiments, but more often to experiment combined with introspection. For instance, asking a question or pronouncing a word, he inquires what ideas, images, etc., this has suggested to the subject. The

[8] Galton, in his *Inquiries into Human Faculty*, has conducted inquiries, interpreted according to the rules of statistics, on mental imagery considered in itself. The question for us would be to have a similar inquest on imagery as a help to thought.

[9] *Etude Expérimentale de l'Intelligence*, Paris (1903).

method has been criticized and indeed there is the objection
which can be advanced against almost every kind of psychological experiment, viz., an involuntary suggestion
from the experimenter himself. This, however, is not to be
feared when the results are of an unexpected nature as
some have been for Binet. As a matter of fact, Binet's
method is considered by psychologists as not being invalidated by that or analogous objections, to which convincing
answers have been given by Bühler;[10] and a somewhat similar method was used, a little later, by the so-called Wurtz-
bourg school. Its creation, however, belongs to Binet.

In Binet's experiments, the question of words is dealt
with incidentally. The answer on that point is favorable
to Galton against Max Müller. To one of the girls,[11] an
answer in words appears as "an image which cuts thought."
Thought is something which appears to her suddenly like
any kind of feeling.

What is more unexpected is that even the intervention of
images is minimized, contrary to Taine's theory. The precision of the answer is striking.[12] "In order to get images,
I must no longer have anything to think of. They [ideas
and images] are separated from each other and never come
together. I never have any images when a word suggests to
me a very great number of thoughts. I must wait for a
while. When, with respect to this word, I have exhausted
every thought, then images come and if thoughts begin
again, the images fade, and alternate."

On that point, Binet himself concludes: "Later on, I

[10] *Archiv f. die Ges. Psych.*, Vol. IX (1907); Vol. XII (1908) especially pp. 93-123. See G. Dumas' *Traité de Psychologie*, Vol. I, Chap.
IV and Vol. II, pp. 113 ff.
[11] *Etude Expérimentale de l'Intelligence*, p. 107.
[12] *ibid.*, p. 124.

was able to convince myself that Armande was quite right; I admit that there exists a kind of antagonism between image and reflection, the more so when the image is very intense. It is in revery and dream that the finest images arise." There is also the fact, observed by Galton and others, that women and children have finer images than adult men who are superior in reflection.

Later experiments by Dwelshauvers (*Les Mécanismes Subconscients*), carried on with students, led to the same main conclusions as Binet's about the conditions of the apparition of images. He finds that images appear only if we give our ideas uncontrolled freedom, i.e., when we are dreaming while awake. As soon as full consciousness, voluntary consciousness, returns, images weaken, darken; they seem to withdraw into some unknown region.

Mental Pictures in Tense Thought. More recent authors (Delacroix, James Angell, Titchener, Varendonck, etc.) have also treated that same subject of words and images in thought. Most of their works, however, will not directly occupy us, on account of a distinction which is especially necessary in our subject.

Psychologists have already distinguished between two kinds of thought. There is "free" thought, which takes place when you let your thoughts wander, without directing them toward any special goal; and there is "controlled" thought, when such a direction is given.[13] The second term is not precise enough for our purpose. There is already a direction in your thought when you are asked what is the date; but the case of inventive thought is obviously differ-

13 R. S. Woodworth, *Psychology* (4th edition, 1940), p. 33. However, Woodworth speaks of your being asked a *difficult* question, which would mean our third case of the tense thought, rather than the simply controlled one.

ent. It requires a certain effort of concentration; it is not only controlled, but tense.

There is no reason why the processes of those three kinds of thought should be the same; and actually they are not. The last case is the only one which directly concerns us.

Binet's View. As a conclusion to his series of experiments, Binet is[14] inclined to think that words or sensorial images may be useful for giving a precise form to feelings or thoughts which, without both these helps, would remain too vague; even, to give us a full consciousness of that thought which would, otherwise, remain an unconscious act of mind; in order to allow the passage of ideas from unconscious to conscious: more precisely, from the unconscious where they are somewhat vague to consciousness where they acquire precision.

I was myself inclined, for a while, to admit that conception of Binet. Indeed, it satisfied to a certain extent the double and seemingly contradictory condition:

(a) That the help of images is absolutely necessary for conducting my thought.

(b) That I am never deceived and even never fear to be deceived by them.

However, further reflection led me to a different conception. Indeed, the case of Binet's or Dwelshauvers' experiments is not ours; it deals with a controlled thought, but not with a tense one. The two girls are asked such questions as, "What appears in your mind when you think of what you did yesterday?" The most difficult question, as far as I could see on examining Binet's book, was, "Think of what you would like to do if you could remain three hours by yourself, being completely free in your actions?"

[14] *Etude Expérimentale de l'Intelligence,* p. 108.

Personal Observations. The case of research work is, of course, very different, for which reason I have wished to understand what takes place in my own mind when I undertake to build up or to comprehend—I have said in the beginning that there is no essential difference—a mathematical argument.

I insist that words are totally absent from my mind when I really think and I shall completely align my case with Galton's in the sense that even after reading or hearing a question, every word disappears at the very moment I am beginning to think it over; words do not reappear in my consciousness[15] before I have accomplished or given up the research, just as happened to Galton; and I fully agree with Schopenhauer when he writes, "Thoughts die the moment they are embodied by words."

I think it also essential to emphasize that I behave in this way not only about words, but even about algebraic signs. I use them when dealing with easy calculations; but whenever the matter looks more difficult, they become too heavy

---

[15] It is quite possible, and rather probable, that words are present in fringe-consciousness. Such is the case, I imagine, for me as concerns words used in mathematics. I doubt, however, that it is so for some other kind of thought because, if it were, I should have less difficulty in finding them. An evident misunderstanding as to the meaning of the question occurs when, after citing William Hamilton who observes that "a cognition must have been already there before it could receive a sign," so that the idea must necessarily precede the word, Max Müller claims to be in agreement (*sic*) with him, because William Hamilton's statement means an "almost contemporaneous" progress of thinking and naming. Though being only an occasional psychologist, I know enough to understand that mental processes are often rapid ones and that it would be absurd to study them without distinguishing between "almost contemporaneous" and simultaneous states. Besides, William Hamilton expresses his feeling on the question in a striking way, saying: "Speech is thus not the mother, but the godmother of knowledge."

a baggage for me. I use concrete representations, but of a quite different nature.

One example of this kind is already known in the history of science. It was given by Euler, in order to explain to a Swedish princess the properties of syllogism. He represents general ideas by circles; then if we are to think of two categories of things, A and B, such that every A is a B, we shall imagine a circle A lying inside a circle B. If, on the contrary, we are told that no A is a B, we shall imagine the circle A as lying completely outside B; while if some A's are B's and some not, the two circles ought to be intersecting ones. Now, personally, if I had to think of any syllogism, I should not think of it in terms of words—words would hardly allow me to see whether the syllogism would be right or wrong—but with a representation analogous to Euler's, only not using circles, but spots of an undefined form, no precise shape being necessary for me to think of spots lying inside or outside of each other.

To consider a slightly less simple case, let us take an elementary and well-known proof in arithmetic, the theorem to be proved being: "The sequel of prime numbers is unlimited." I shall repeat the successive steps of the classic proof of that theorem, writing, opposite each of them, the corresponding mental picture in my mind. We have, for instance, to prove that there is a prime greater than 11.

STEPS IN THE PROOF	MY MENTAL PICTURES
I consider all primes from 2 to 11, say 2, 3, 5, 7, 11.	I see a confused mass.
I form their product $2 \times 3 \times 5 \times 7 \times 11 = N$	N being a rather large number, I imagine a point rather remote from the confused mass.

I increase that product by 1, say N plus 1.	I see a second point a little beyond the first.
That number, if not a prime, must admit of a prime divisor, which is the required number.	I see a place somewhere between the confused mass and the first point.

What may be the use of such a strange and cloudy imagery? Certainly, it is not meant to remind me of any property of divisibility, prime numbers and so on. This is most important because any such information which it could give me would be likely to be more or less inaccurate and to deceive me. Thus, that mechanism satisfies condition (b) previously required. On the contrary, this condition is but partly satisfied by Binet's hypothesis: giving precision to unconscious ideas would always risk altering them.

But at the same time, one can easily realize how such a mechanism or an analogous one may be necessary to me for the understanding of the above proof. I need it in order to have a simultaneous view of all elements of the argument, to hold them together, to make a whole of them—in short, to achieve that synthesis which we spoke of in the beginning of this section and give the problem its physiognomy. It does not inform me on any link of the argument (i.e., on any property of divisibility or primes); but it reminds me how these links are to be brought together. If we still follow Poincaré's comparison, that imagery is necessary in order that the useful hookings, once obtained, may not get lost.

Indeed, every mathematical research compels me to build such a schema, which is always and must be of a vague character, so as not to be deceptive. I shall give one less elementary example from my first researches (my thesis). I had to consider a sum of an infinite number of terms, intending to valuate its order of magnitude. In that case, there is a group of terms which chances to be predominant, all others having a negligible influence. Now, when I think of that question, I see not the formula itself, but the place it would take if written: a kind of ribbon, which is thicker or darker at the place corresponding to the possibly important terms; or (at other moments), I see something like a formula, but by no means a legible one, as I should see it (being strongly long-sighted) if I had no eye-glasses on, with letters seeming rather more apparent (though still *not legible*) at the place which is supposed to be the important one.

I have been told by some friends that I have a special way of looking when indulging in mathematical research. I hardly doubt that this especially accompanies the construction of the schema in question.

This is in connection with the question of intellectual fatigue. I have asked some prominent physiologists, especially Louis Lapicque, how intellectual work can produce fatigue, as no "work," in the physicist's meaning of the word, seems to be produced. Lapicque's opinion is that intellectual work ought to be comparable to nothing more than the act of turning the pages of a book. However, intellectual fatigue exists: from the objective and physiological point of view, it has been studied in an important book of Binet and Victor Henri. That part of the question is beyond my sphere. From the psychological point of view, it can be considered as certain that, similarly to what we have said of Rodin's case, fatigue corresponds to the effort for synthesis, to the fact of giving the research its unity and, therefore, at least in my case, to the constitution of a proper schema.

One or two observations can be added:

If I should use a blackboard and write the expression $2 \times 3 \times 5 \times 7 \times 11$, the above described schema would disappear from my mind as having obviously become useless, and would be automatically replaced by the formula which I should have before my eyes.

Then I must observe that I distinctly belong to the auditory type;[16] and precisely on that account my mental pictures are exclusively visual. The reason for that is quite clear to me: such visual pictures are more naturally vague, as we have seen it to be necessary in order to lead me without misleading me.

I also add that the case we have just examined especially concerns arithmetical, algebraic or analytic studies. When I undertake some geometrical research, I have generally a mental view of the diagram itself, though generally an inadequate or incomplete one, in spite of which it affords the necessary synthesis—a tendency which, it would ap-

---

[16] I have a rather bad memory of physiognomies and am much exposed to failures of recognition or false recognitions; on the contrary, I am very sensitive to the sound of names, being much more desirous to see such rivers as the Mohawk or the Mattawamkeag than even their beauty would warrant, because their mere names call to my mind the idea of forests and Indian life. Also, I am rather less sensible than others to likenesses in faces and rather more sensible to likenesses in voices.

Many mistakes by automatic writing (see Section II, p. 22) are due to auditory mental images. Examples of that kind are classic. Personally, they are frequent in my case: my conscious ego dictates to my unconscious one, which writes a word instead of another one if their sounds are somewhat alike. While writing the present work, I remember to have written "simple" instead of "same place" and "will she" instead of "we shall." I should think that such auditive mistakes are more frequent on my part when I am writing in English than in French—quite naturally.

pear, results from a training which goes back to my very earliest childhood.

Paradoxical as it seems, it very often happens that, in those geometrical problems, I use successfully a process quite opposite to the synthesis I have explained in what precedes. I happen to abstract some special part of the diagram and consider it apart from the rest, this consideration leading to a "relay-result." The whole argument is, nevertheless, even in that case, grasped as a unique entity, as a synthesis into which such a relay-result, if existent, is included. That is a process which, according to Pierre Boutroux[17] (see below), Descartes says is frequent in Greek geometry.

Respective Roles of Full Consciousness and Fringe-Consciousness. The above observations concern the functioning of thought when it is intensely concentrated, be it in an entirely conscious work or in a conscious preliminary work.

Now, as we have explained at the end of Section II, that very concentration gives us a possibility of distinguishing between full consciousness and fringe-consciousness, a distinction which is rather difficult in other circumstances, but which, in that case, is rather easily accessible to observation.

What does observation give as to the phenomena just described?

It could be supposed a priori that the links of the argument exist in full consciousness, the corresponding images being thought of by the subconscious. My personal introspection undoubtedly leads me to the contrary conclusion: my consciousness is focused on the successive images, or more exactly, on the global image; the arguments themselves wait, so to speak, in the antechamber (see p. 25) to

17 P. Boutroux, however, gives no precise reference.

be introduced at the beginning of the "precising" phase.

This instance most clearly illustrates the nature and role of the fringe-consciousness, which is, so to speak, at the service of full consciousness, being ready to appear in it whenever wanted.

Other Stages of Research. What happens when there is a period of incubation: in other words, an action of the deeper unconscious? Of course, no direct answer is available; but a strong presumption that there is some mechanism of an analogous kind at work results from the fact that it seems to be the fittest one to satisfy the double condition (a), (b) which is to be fulfilled.

I should even interpret in a similar way the case of illumination. When I think of the example mentioned in Section I (see page 8) I see a schematic diagram: a square of whose sides only the verticals are drawn and, inside of it, four points being the vertices of a rectangle and joined by (hardly apparent) diagonals—a diagram the symbolic meaning of which will be clear for technicians. It even seems to me that such was my visualization of the question in 1892, as far as I can recollect. Of course, remembrances going back half a century are not quite reliable; however, we recognized symbolic diagrams as being essential to a synthetic view of questions, and it seems to me that such a synthetic view is at least as necessary in cases of illumination as in conscious work. If we admit this line of reasoning, illumination would be transmitted from a lesser or greater depth of unconsciousness to fringe-consciousness, which would have it represented by a symbolic diagram in the conscious ego.

That image and its meaning are in some way connected and, at the same time, independent, is observed by Watt,

Archiv. f.d. Ges. Psych., 1904, Vol. IV (see G. Dumas'
Traité de Psychologie, Vol. I, Chap. IV). It seems to me
that such a kind of simultaneous connection and independence is enlightened by the intervention of fringe-consciousness.

Then comes the verifying and "precising" stage. In that
final phase of the work, I may use algebraic symbols; but,
rather often, I do not use them in the usual and regular
way. I do not take time to write the equations completely,
only caring to see, so to speak, how they look. These equations, or some terms of them, are often disposed in a peculiar and funny order like actors in a scenario, by means of
which they "speak" to me, as long as I continue to consider
them. But if, after having been interrupted in my calculations, I resume them on the following day, what I have written in that way is as if "dead" for me. Generally, I can do
nothing else than throw the sheet away and begin everything anew, except if, in the first day, I have obtained one
or two formulae which I have fully verified and can use as
relay-formulae.

As to words, they remain absolutely absent from my
mind until I come to the moment of communicating the
results in written or oral form, or (very exceptionally) for
relay-results; in the latter case, they may, as William
Hamilton observes, be the intermediary "necessary to give
stability to our intellectual process, to establish each step
in our advance as a new starting point for our advance to
another beyond"—in which William Hamilton is right but
for the fact that any relay-result can play such a role.[18]

[18] William Hamilton uses an interesting comparison to the process of
tunneling through a sand bank. "In this operation, it is impossible to
succeed unless every foot, nay, almost every inch in our progress be

Another Conception. After having acquired some information about the behaviorist school, I wondered how behaviorist doctrine dealt with our present question and whether it agreed with my observations. I understand that, for behaviorism, we do not necessarily think in words, but that, otherwise, our thought may consist of muscular motions, such as a shrug of the shoulders, motions of the eyelids or the eyes, etc.

I have no recollection of such kind of motions connected with my research work. Of course, I cannot watch my motions while deeply engaged in research, but witnesses of my daily life and work can assert that they never saw anything of that kind. They have only observed the special "inside" look which I often happen to have when plunged in deeply concentrated reflection. What I can say is that I do not see what kind of motions could help me to get a clear view of more or less difficult reasonings, while, on the contrary, we have seen that proper mental pictures can evidently be helpful for that.

An Inquiry among Mathematicians. It is natural to investigate, with respect to our present subject, the behavior of mathematicians in general. Unhappily, I was unable to learn about French mathematicians, having thought of the question only after my departure from Europe.

About the mathematicians born or resident in America, whom I asked, phenomena are mostly analogous to those

secured by an arch of masonry before we attempt the excavation of another. Now, language is to the mind precisely what the arch is to the tunnel. The power of thinking and the power of excavation are not dependent on the words in the one case, on the mason-work in the other; but without these subsidiaries, neither process could be carried on beyond its rudimentary commencement."

More generally, the function thus described belongs to what we have called relay-results. In inventive effort, those do not always imply words.

which I have noticed in my own case.[19] Practically all of them—contrary to what occasional inquiries had suggested to Galton as to the man in the street—avoid not only the use of mental words but also, just as I do, the mental use of algebraic or any other precise signs; also as in my case, they use vague images. There are two or three exceptional cases, the most important of which is the mathematician George D. Birkhoff, one of the greatest in the world, who is accustomed to visualize algebraic symbols and to work with them mentally. Norbert Wiener's answer is that he happens to think either with or without words. Jessie Douglas generally thinks without words or algebraic signs. Eventually, his research thought is in connection with words, but only with their rhythm, a kind of Morse language where only the numbers of syllables of some words appear. This, of course, has nothing in common with Max Müller's thesis and is rather analogous to Galton's use of meaningless words.

G. Pólya's case—I intend to speak only of men who have made quite significant discoveries—is different. He does make an eventual use of words. "I believe," he writes to me, "that the decisive idea which brings the solution of a problem is rather often connected with a well-turned word or sentence. The word or the sentence enlightens the situation, gives things, as you say, a physiognomy. It can precede by little the decisive idea or follow on it immediately; perhaps, it arises at the same time as the decisive idea. . . . The right word, the subtly appropriate word, helps us to recall the mathematical idea, perhaps less completely and less objectively than a diagram or a mathe-

[19] At the moment of printing, a letter from Professor Einstein reaches me, containing information of capital interest. See Appendix II.

matical notation, but in an analogous way. . . . It may contribute to fix it in the mind." Moreover, he finds that a proper notation—that is, a properly chosen letter to denote a mathematical quantity—can give him similar help; and some kind of puns, whether of good or poor quality, may be useful for that purpose. For instance, Pólya, teaching in German at a Swiss university, usually made his junior students observe that z and w are the initials of the German words "Zahl" and "Wert," which precisely denote the respective roles which z and w had to play in the theory which he was explaining.

That case of Pólya seems to be quite exceptional (I did not meet with any similar one among the other men who answered me).[20] Even he, however, does not use words as equivalents of ideas, since he uses *one* word or one or two letters to symbolize a whole line of thought; his psychological process would be in agreement with Stanley's statement[21] that "language, as an indicator, can only indicate by suggesting to our consciousness what is indicated, as object, thought or feeling, even in most summary and unself-conscious form to which it is brought by practice."

The mental pictures of the mathematicians whose answers I have received are most frequently visual, but they may also be of another kind—for instance, kinetic. There can also be auditive ones, but even these, as the example of J. Douglas shows, quite generally keep their vague character.[22] For B. O. Koopman, "images have a symbolic rather

[20] I have just heard of the rather analogous case of Professor Chevalley.

[21] *Psychological Review*, Vol. IV (1891), p. 71. In that place, Stanley chiefly deals with poetical invention, where the role of words is evidently more important than elsewhere.

[22] One of my colleagues of Columbia writes to me that his mathematical thought is usually accompanied by visual images and hardly ever by words other than vague exclamations of surprise, irritation, elation, etc.

than a diagrammatic relation to the mathematical ideas"
which are considered, a description whose analogy with the
above is evident. Professor Koopman's observations also
agree with mine on the fact that such images appear in full
consciousness while the corresponding arguments provisionally remain in the "antechamber."

We can say as much of the observations which Ribot[23]
has gathered by questioning mathematicians. Some of them
have told him that they think in a purely algebraic way,
with the help of signs; others *always* need a "figurated representation," a "construction," even if this is "considered
as pure fiction."

Some Ideas of Descartes. In the *Regulae ad Directionem
Ingenii*, which, in their second half (from the 14th rule
on), deal with the role of imagination in science, Descartes
seems to have conceived the idea of processes similar to
those we speak of. At least, this can be induced from some
places of the analysis of the *Regulae* made by Pierre Boutroux.[24] For instance, he is reported by Pierre Boutroux to
have said that "Imagination, by itself, is unable to create
Science, but we must, in certain cases have recourse to it.
First, by focusing it on the object we want to consider, we
prevent it from going astray and, moreover, it can be useful in awakening within us certain ideas." Again, "Imagination will chiefly be of great use in solving a problem by
several deductions, the results of which need to be coordi-
nated after a complete enumeration. Memory is necessary
to retain the data of the problem if we do not use them all
from the beginning. We should risk forgetting them if the

23 *Evolution des Idées Générales*, p. 143.

24 *L'Imagination et les Mathématiques selon Descartes*, Bibl. de la
Faculté des Lettres de Paris, Vol. 10 (1900).

image of the objects under consideration were not constantly present to our mind and did not offer all of them to us at each instant."

This is the role of images as we described it above. However, Descartes distrusts that intervention of imagination and wishes to eliminate it completely from science. He even reproaches ancient geometry for having used it. He wants to eliminate imagination from every branch of science by reducing all of them to mathematics (which he tried to do, but did not succeed in doing), mathematics consisting, more than any other science, of pure understanding.

To see what we must think of such an idea, we need only recall how Descartes' program has been carried out by modern mathematicians. First, as is well known, geometry can be completely reduced to numerical combinations by the help of analytical geometry which Descartes himself created. But we have just seen that deductions in the realm of numbers may be, at least in several mathematical minds, most generally accompanied by images.

More recently, another rigorous treatment of the principles of geometry, which, logically speaking, has been fully freed from any appeal to intuition, has been developed on quite different bases by the celebrated mathematician Hilbert. His beginning, which is now classic among mathematicians, is "Let us consider three systems of things. The things composing the first system, we will call *points*; those of the second, we will call *straight lines*, and those of the third system, we will call *planes*," clearly meaning that we ought by no means to inquire what those "things" may represent.

Logically, of course—and this is all that is essential— the result announced is fully attained and every interven-

tion of geometrical sense eliminated: that is, theoretically
unnecessary to follow the reasoning from the beginning to
the end. Is it the same from the psychological point of view?
Certainly not. There is no doubt that Hilbert, in working
out his *Principles of Geometry*, has been constantly
guided by his geometrical sense. If anybody could doubt
that (which no mathematician will), he ought simply to
cast one glance at Hilbert's book. Diagrams appear at
practically every page. They do not hamper mathematical
readers in ascertaining that, logically speaking, no concrete picture is needed.[25]

This is again a case where one is guided by images without being enslaved by them, and it is again possible (at
least in my own case) thanks to the same division of work
between proper consciousness and fringe-consciousness.[26]

Similarly, Descartes censures the habit noticed by him in
Greek geometers (see above) of considering separately one
part of a diagram. There is no reason for that objection.
We meet with the same confusion between logical and psychological processes. The method in question no more compromises the rigor of the argument than the image mentioned above compromises the proof of the fact that prime
numbers form an unlimited sequel.

[25] There is already a paradox, as Klein notices, in the fact that we can
reason on an angle equal to the millionth part of a second, though we are
completely unable to distinguish between the sides of such an angle; and
its discussion (*Revue de Métaphysique et de Morale* [1908], p. 923) by
Winter, one of the philosophers who had the best understanding of
scientific subjects, shows the analogy of that circumstance with our observations in the text.

[26] Another instance, which we shall meet in Section VII (see p. 103
note) will illustrate this even more clearly and convincingly. Indeed,
in the latter instance of Section VII, no doubt can subsist (at least as
concerns my own mind) on the way the division of work mentioned in
the text takes place.

Other Thinkers. We do not have many data on that question in fields other than the mathematical one. It is curious that, according to the above-mentioned work of Binet (*Etude Expérimentale de l'Intelligence*, pp. 127-129), even in free thought, vague images may occur as representatives of more precise ideas.

An instance quite analogous to our above description is that of the economist Sidgwick, which he himself reported at the International Congress of Experimental Psychology, in 1892. His reasonings on economic questions were almost always accompanied by images, and "the images were often curiously arbitrary and sometimes almost undecipherably symbolic. For example, it took him a long time to discover that an odd, symbolic image which accompanied the word 'value' was a faint, partial image of a man putting something on a scale." Also a most curious process occurs among musical composers, according to Julius Bahle (*Der Musikalische Schaffensprozess*, Leipzig, Hirzel, 1936; quoted by Delacroix, *L'Invention et le Génie*, p. 520). Several of them see their creations in their initial conception, in a visual form (inspiration is what he calls a "Tonvision"). One of them perceives in that way, without any precise musical presentation, "the main line and main characteristics of his music. Besides, it is perhaps rather difficult to say to what extent music is absent from that formal schema."[27]

I have asked only a few men belonging to other branches of mental activity. The answers have been various and I

[27] A painter tells me that, in the first phase of composition, his visual images are voluntarily vague.

cannot assert that results could not differ from our previous ones.[28]

Some scientists have told me of mental pictures quite analogous to those which we have described. For instance,[29] Professor Claude Levi-Strauss, when thinking about a difficult question in his ethnographic studies, sees, as I do, unprecise and schematic pictures which, moreover, have the remarkable character of being three-dimensional. Also, asking a few chemists, all of them reported absolutely wordless thought, with the help of mental pictures.

The physiologist André Mayer's mind behaves quite differently. He tells me that his thought immediately appears to him in a fully formulated form, so that no effort whatever is necessary to him in order to write it down.

It would be interesting to know how medical men behave, in that respect, in the difficult act of arriving at a diagnosis. I had the opportunity of asking a prominent one, and he told me that he thinks without words in that case, though his thought uses words in theoretical and scientific studies.

A type of thinking which seems surprising at first has been discovered by the psychologist Ribot,[30] who finds it

[28] Our statesman Aristide Briand, according to what was observed by one of his closest collaborators who was able to see him often at work, did not think in words when he planned his speeches. Words appeared only at the very moment of pronouncing them.

It would certainly be worth while to know about the opinion of some important military leaders. There could be no case where a simultaneous view of the synthesis and of every detail would be more essential.

[29] Such is also the case of Professor Roman Jakobson (see p. 96).

[30] *L'Evolution des Idées Générales*, p. 143. Jean Perrin, according to information given to me by his son, had *intermittently* pictures of the typographic-visual type; Francis Perrin generally thinks without words; but, from time to time, a word appears to him. Sidgwick's ideas appeared in typographic-visual representations when, instead of economic subjects, he was thinking of mathematics or logic.

to be more frequent than would be expected. It is what he calls the "typographic visual type" and consists in seeing mentally ideas in the form of corresponding printed words. The first discovery of this by Ribot was the case of a man whom he mentions as a well-known physiologist. For that man, even the words "dog, animal" (while he was living among dogs and experimenting on them daily) were not accompanied by any image, but were seen by him as being printed. Similarly, when he heard the name of an intimate friend, he saw it printed and had to make an effort to see the image of this friend. It was the same with the word "water," and carbonic acid or hydrogen appeared to his mind either by their printed full names or by their printed chemical symbol. Being strongly surprised by that statement, the sincerity and accuracy of which were not to be doubted, Ribot later on observed that that case was by no means a unique one and similar ones were to be found in several people.

Moreover, according to Ribot, men belonging to that typographic-visual type cannot conceive how other people's thought can proceed differently.

This is the state of mind which we have already noticed in Max Müller himself as concerns, more generally, thought in words and which is really stupefying when we find it among men accustomed to dealing with philosophical matters. How can we wonder that people have been burned alive on account of differences in theological opinions, when we see that a first-rate man like Max Müller, apropos of a harmless question of psychology, uses scornful words toward his old master Lotze, for having written that the

logical meaning of a given proposition is in itself independent of the form in which language expresses it?[31]

Thus, we have let ourselves be induced to deal with a
chapter of psychology rather different from the one which
is our main object. Some parts of this section could be
called "A case of psychological incomprehension."

This is not at all the only instance of the double fact:
(1) that the psychology of different individuals may differ in some essential points; (2) that, if so, it may be almost impossible for the one to conceive the state of mind of
the other.[32]

Is Thought in words without inconvenience? Of course,
I must myself be on my guard against the same lack of

[31] Max Müller concedes that he can "with some effort" enter into the
mind of a decided adversary like Berkeley, "a kind of philosophical hal-
lucination," to use his own words. But he cannot understand the opinion
that *most* of our thoughts are carried on in language but not quite all, or
that *most* people think in words but not all. That some of the greatest
writers may have said that not from "lack of courage" but because facts
are like that, visibly lies beyond his imagination.

[32] Paradoxical as it seems, there are two such instances in the domain
of mathematics. Some years before World War I, a question which,
though a mathematical one, was contiguous to metaphysics raised a lively
discussion among some of us, especially between myself and one of my
best and most respected friends, the great scientist Lebesgue. We could
not avoid the conclusion that evidence—that starting point of certitude
in every order of thinking—did not have the same meaning for him and
for me. Only, of course, we were never tempted to despise each other
merely because we recognized the impossibility of understanding each
other.

The subject in question belonged to the theory of "sets." Now, when,
in 1879-1884, Georg Cantor communicated his fundamental results on
that theory (now one of the bases of contemporary science), one of them
looked so paradoxical and upset so radically all our fundamental notions
that it unleashed the decided hostility of Kroneker, one of the leading
mathematicians in that time, who prevented Cantor from getting any
new appointment in German universities and even from having any
memoir published in German periodicals. Of course, the proof of that
result is as clear and rigorous as any other proof in mathematics, leaving no possibility of not admitting it.

comprehension. Certainly, I must confess my incomprehension of the fact that the typographic-visual type or other verbal types are possible, and I can hardly refrain from thinking of Goethe's verses:

> "Denn wo Begriffe fehlen,
> Da stellt ein Wort zur rechten Zeit sich ein."

But I cannot forget that such men as Max Müller and others, not mediocre, think in such a way, though I do not succeed in understanding it. In this connection, I regret that Ribot has not published the name of the physiologist he speaks of, and that we are therefore unable to form any opinion of the value of his work.

For those of us who do not think in words, the chief difficulty in understanding those who do lies in our inability to understand how they can be sure they are not misled by the words they use—see our condition (b), page 74. As Ribot says,[33] "The word much resembles paper money (banknotes, checks, etc.), having the same usefulness and the same dangers."

Such a danger has not remained unnoticed. Locke mentions many men as using words *instead* of ideas, and we have seen that Leibniz cannot help experiencing a certain anxiety as to the influence of thinking in words on the course of his thought.

Curiously enough, Max Müller himself says that indirectly. To Kant, he opposes his friend Hamann, whom he

[33] *The Psychology of Attention*, p. 52 (translation of 1911; p. 85 of the French edition of 1889). Ribot, in that same place, also describes the evolution of that function of the word. He writes, "Learning how to count in the case of children, and, better still, in the case of savages, clearly shows how the word, at first firmly clinging to objects, then to images, progressively detaches itself from them, to live an independent life of its own."

highly praises, and he cites the latter as having written "Language is not only the foundation for the whole faculty of thinking, but the central point also from which proceed the misunderstandings of reason by herself. . . . The question with me is not what is the reason, but what is the language? And here, I suspect, is the ground of the paralogisms and antinomies with which the reason is charged."

This would be all right if, consequently, Max Müller warned us to beware of such misunderstandings caused by language; but on the contrary, he maintains that words, by themselves, could never produce any error. "The word itself is clear and simple and right; we ourselves only derange and huddle and muddle it."

I should not have spoken once more of Max Müller if the statement expressed in that passage of the *Introductory Lectures* did not go even beyond the hitherto examined question of words in thought. Immediately after that citation of Hamann, apparently yielding to a professional deformation, he speaks to us of "the science of thought, founded as it is on the science of language." Will he have us believe that language not only must accompany thought, but must govern it?

Unhappily for his thesis, such a tendency seems not to have been always harmless to him. It requires a man who identifies thought with words to attack Darwin's theory[34] by only taking account of the word "selection" and neglecting, as allegedly a "metaphorical disguise," the meaning of it in Darwin's ideas.

The thinker using mental words may, on the contrary, understand that not only words, but every kind of auxiliary

[34] *The Science of Thought*, Vol. I, p. 97.

signs only play the role of kinds of labels attached to ideas. He will, more or less consciously, apply proper methods (about which it would be interesting to inquire) in order to give them that role and no other one. We have seen that Pólya himself, the only one among the mathematicians I have consulted who makes so much use of words, introduces a single one in a whole course of thought so as to remind himself of a central idea, while Jessie Douglas represents some of them by their mere syllabic rhythm. Similarly, one of my colleagues in literary matters thinks in words, but from time to time introduces a *nonexistent* word. This process, to be compared with Jessie Douglas's or Galton's, seems to me to be evidently useful for the same purpose.

In the thought of Leibniz, we can be sure that such misunderstandings as were dreaded by Hamann could not occur: first, because he is Leibniz, then, because he is aware of the danger. But, though being little acquainted with the theories of metaphysicians, I am rather disquieted on reading in Ribot's *Evolution des Idées Générales* that among them the typographic-visual type seems to be overwhelmingly the most frequent one.

Among philosophers, there seems, indeed, to be a certain tendency to confuse logical thought with the use of words. For instance, it is difficult not to recognize it in William James when he complains[35] that, "we are so subject to the philosophical tradition which treats *logos* or discursive thought generally as the sole avenue to truth, that to fall back on raw unverbalized life has more of a revealer, etc." —the word "unverbalized" hardly leaving any doubt that he has used the word *logos* in the ancient Greek sense.

Is not that tendency likely eventually to mislead those

[35] *A Pluralistic Universe*, p. 272.

who let themselves be governed by it? Reading Fouillée's objections concerning the unconscious in his *Evolutionisme des Idées-Forces* (see Section II, p. 28), I wonder whether he does not mistake words for reasons.

I even feel some uneasiness when I see that Locke and similarly John Stuart Mill consider the use of words necessary whenever complex ideas are implied. I think, on the contrary, and so will a majority of scientific men, that the more complicated and difficult a question is, the more we distrust words, the more we feel we must control that dangerous ally and its sometimes treacherous precision.

A Valuable Description. Though, in the question of words in thought, divergent opinions still occasionally arise, it is now rather generally admitted that words do not need to be present. On the other hand, several recent psychologists, even while insisting on words,[36] have noticed, as we do, the intervention of vague images which do not truly represent but symbolize ideas.[37]

I shall not undertake to review these works; but I cannot resist the temptation to reproduce the highly interesting communication which has been kindly addressed to me by Professor Roman Jakobson, who, besides his well-known linguistic work, takes a fruitful interest in psychological subjects. It reads thus:

"Signs are a necessary support of thought. For socialized thought (stage of communication) and for the thought which is being socialized (stage of formulation), the most usual system of signs is language properly called; but internal thought, especially when creative, willingly uses

[36] See Delacroix, *Le Langage et la Pensée*, pp. 384 ff. and compare the footnote of p. 406.

[37] See also Titchener's *Experimental Psychology of the Thought Processes*, especially Lecture I and corresponding Notes.

other systems of signs which are more flexible, less stand-ardized than language and leave more liberty, more dy-namism to creative thought. . . . Amongst all these signs or symbols, one must distinguish between conventional signs, borrowed from social convention and, on the other hand, personal signs which, in their turn, can be subdivided into constant signs, belonging to general habits, to the individ-ual pattern of the person considered and into episodical signs, which are established ad hoc and only participate in a single creative act."

This remarkably precise and profound analysis beau-tifully enlightens our observations such as we have re-ported above. That there should be such an agreement be-tween minds working in quite different branches is a remarkable fact.

Comparison with Another Question Concerning Imagery. Images constitute, as we could say, the chief subject of Taine's celebrated work *On Intelligence.* He treats them from points of view rather different from ours (as tense thought is rarely, if ever, considered). However, there is, concerning them, a question which particularly interests him and on which the above observations might possibly throw some light. As he persistently notices, it ought to be explained how images appear to us, often very vividly, and nevertheless remain distinct from real sensations; how our mind can generally differentiate between images and hallu-cinations.[38]

But, in our case, we have also a sequel of images develop-ing parallel to thought properly called. Both mental

[38] The same question also assumes great importance in some psycho-logical studies of Varendonck. See his book, *Psychology of Day Dreams,* especially Chap. II, pp. 75-86.

streams, images and reasonings, constantly guide each other though keeping perfectly distinct and even, to a certain extent, independent; and we have found this to be due to a cooperation between proper consciousness and fringe-consciousness. It may be supposed that there is some analogy between the two phenomena and that one could help us to understand the other.

Can Imagery be Educated? The above considerations suggest a question analogous to one which has been raised at the end of Section IV. Is it possible—if desirable—for our volition to influence the nature of the auxiliary signs used by your thought? Now, this has been done. Titchener has carried out a most remarkable attempt in that sense. As he explains to us,[39] his natural tendency would have been to employ internal speech; but he has always tried and always succeeded in having a wide range and a great variety of imagery, "fearing that, as one gets older, one tends also to become more and more verbal in type."

That too great importance of verbal intervention in his thought is thus prevented by a constant renewing of imagery. What is more curious, he uses for such a purpose not only visual images but, above all, auditory, viz., musical ones.

But he uses also the help of visual imagery, "which is always at my disposal," he says, "and which I can mould and direct at will." "Reading any work, I instinctively arrange the facts or arguments in some visual pattern and I am as likely to think in terms of this pattern as I am to think in words," and the better the work suits such a pattern, the better it is understood.

Such an auto-education of mental processes seems to me

[39] *Experimental Psychology of the Thought Processes*, pp. 7 ff.

to be one of the most remarkable achievements in psychology.

Using Relay-results. It is obvious that the necessary synthesis is greatly simplified when some parts of the deduction are replaced by the corresponding relay-results, which are in this case especially important.[40]

General Remarks. All this concerns men engaged in intellectual work. Investigation among other groups seems to meet the difficulty that, as we have seen, the laws of tense thought may be and seem to be very different from those of usual and common ideation, which is the only frequent one among ordinary people. This is probably the reason why Galton, though seeing the necessity of a more general inquiry, was unable to make it.

At any rate, we see that, while what we said in the preceding sections seems to be common to various creative minds, the nature of auxiliary concrete representations may vary considerably from one mind to the other.

Addendum. The distinction between full consciousness and fringe-consciousness has not been easily perceived by several scientists, and I feel it necessary to elaborate this point. Just after having constructed a deduction, I can easily remember what has taken place during its development; and, so doing, I generally realize that *at no instant* had the properly-called reasoning been present to my conscious ego, which had considered nothing else than the above-described schema, only "fishing" each piece of the logical construction when the proper time had come.

---

[40] This is a peculiar feature of mathematical thought, by which it differs from other kinds of meditation. It is clear that only mathematical deduction allows us to leave a proof completely aside and replace it by its conclusion. In other cases it does not happen that the latter may be "mathematically" equivalent to its premises.

VII. DIFFERENT KINDS OF
MATHEMATICAL MINDS

THE PHENOMENA considered in Sections I-V seem to happen similarly in many mathematical research scholars. On the contrary, concrete representations studied in the preceding section were far from the same for everybody. This section will also be devoted to differences among various ways of mathematical thinking. It will have to our former considerations the same relation which the distinction between various zoological genera and species has to general physiology.

The Case of Common Sense. Let us start from the beginning, that is from the case of people simply reasoning with their common sense. In that case, we can say that much is afforded by the unconscious and little is asked from further conscious elaboration.

It often happens, besides, that that unconscious is a very superficial one and its data are not essentially different from regular reasoning. Thus, Spencer, alluding to the classic syllogism "every man is mortal;—now, Peter is a man;—therefore, Peter is mortal," supposes that you hear of a ninety-year-old man who undertakes to build a new house for himself. Spencer has no difficulty in proving that the syllogism is really present in your fringe-consciousness and that, between it and the stream of thought—an instantaneous one, as is general in unconsciousness—which leads you to speak of the man as being unreasonable, there is but a difference of form. Things can happen similarly in the case of many simple mathematical deductions.

In other instances, however, ways followed by common

sense may be very different from those which we can formulate by explicit reasoning. It happens especially in questions of a concrete nature—say, geometrical or mechanical
ones. Our ideas on such subjects, acquired in early childhood, seem to be relegated to a remote unconsciousness; we
cannot know them exactly and it is probable that they
often imply empirical reasons, taken not from true reasoning but from the experience of our senses. Let us take one
or two examples.

Let us imagine that I throw what is called a "material
point"—that is, a very small body, such as a very small
marble—which will go on moving on account of its initial
velocity and its weight. Common sense tells us that the
motion must take place in a vertical plane, the vertical
plane P drawn through the initial line of projection. In
that case, it is hardly doubtful that the subconscious reasoning uses the "principle of sufficient reason," there being
no reason why the movable point should go to the right
rather than to the left side of the aforesaid plane P.

The mathematical proof, such as classically given in
courses of rational mechanics, proceeds in an utterly different way, with the use of several theorems of the differential and integral calculus. It is to be noticed, however, that
the proof which occurs to common sense could be transformed into a perfectly rigorous one, by applying a general theorem (also belonging to the integral calculus)
which says that under the aforesaid conditions (the direction and magnitude of the initial velocity being given) the
motion is uniquely determined. That theorem, in its turn,
can be rigorously proved; but the latter proof takes place
only in higher courses of calculus, so that, in regular teaching, the way suggested by common sense to reach our con-

clusions appears actually less elementary than the other one.

Let us now consider two examples in geometry. If I think of drawing a curve in a plane, by the continuous motion of a point, it is a fact of common sense that at all of its points (some exceptional ones being perhaps excepted) that curve will admit of a tangent (in other words, that, at every instant, the motion must take place in some determined direction). We do not know how our common sense, i.e., our unconscious, reaches such a conclusion: perhaps by empiricism, i.e., by memory of the lines we are accustomed to see or, as F. Klein supposes, by a confusion of geometrical curves, which have no thickness whatever, with the lines which we can actually draw and which always have some thickness. As a matter of fact, the conclusion is false; mathematicians can construct continuous curves which have no tangent at any point.

In the second place, let us consider a plane closed curve which has no "double point," that is, which nowhere intersects itself. It is evident to common sense that such a curve, whatever its shape may be, divides the plane (a) into two different regions; (b) into not more than two.

How common sense elaborates that conclusion, is not positively known, intervention of empiricism being again probable. This time, the conclusion (Jordan's theorem) is correct; but, evident as it is for our common sense, its proof is of great difficulty.

By such examples as these two, it has been realized that, at least in a certain class of questions relating to principles,[1] we cannot surely rely on our ordinary space-intui-

1 The questions we are alluding to depend on arithmetization rather than on Hilbert's ideas such as mentioned in Section VI.

tion: as geometrical properties can always be reconducted to numerical ones, thanks to the invention of analytical geometry, arguments should always be fully arithmetized, or, at least, it must be ascertained that this arithmetization, if not given at length for brevity's sake, is possible. Pascal's word "Tout ce qui passe la Géométrie nous passe" is replaced, for the modern mathematician, by "Tout ce qui passe l'Arithmétique nous passe."

For instance, a proof of Jordan's theorem, which we have just enunciated, is not satisfactory if not fully arithmetizable.[2]

Second Step: the Student in Mathematics. After that common-sense state of human thought, there has come the scientific state. We have seen that it is characterized by the intervention of the threefold operation of verifying the result; "precising" it; and, above all, making it utilizable, which, as we have seen, requires the enunciation of relay-results. We have seen that that too is essential, first for the certitude of the knowledge thus acquired; then, for its fruitfulness and the possibility of extending it.

These characters can help us to understand what takes place, psychologically speaking, in the passage from the

----

[2] Same remark on this subject as on Hilbert's *Principles*. I have given a simplified proof of part (a) of Jordan's theorem. Of course, my proof is completely arithmetizable (otherwise it would be considered nonexistent); but, investigating it, I never ceased thinking of the diagram (only thinking of a very twisted curve), and so do I still when remembering it. I cannot even say that I explicitly verified or verify every link of the argument as to its being arithmetizable (in other words, the arithmetized argument *does not* generally appear in my full consciousness). However, that each link can be arithmetized is unquestionable as well for me as for any mathematician who will read the proof: I can give it instantly in its arithmetized form, which proves that that arithmetized form is present in my fringe-consciousness.

former state to the latter: in other words, what concerns the case of the student of mathematics.

How commonly total misunderstandings and failures occur in that case, is well known. I shall, besides, be very brief on that subject, because it has been profoundly treated by Poincaré (*Les Définitions dans l'Enseignement* in *Science et Méthode*). Even before quoting him, it is not useless to observe that that case of the mathematical student already belongs to our subject of invention. Between the work of the student who tries to solve a problem in geometry or algebra and a work of invention, one can say that there is only a difference of degree, a difference of level, both works being of a similar nature.

Now, how does it happen that so many are incapable of that work, incapable of understanding mathematics? That is what Poincaré examines and of which he in a striking way shows the true reason which lies in the meaning that ought to be given to the word "to understand."

"To understand the demonstration of a theorem, is that to examine successively each syllogism composing it and ascertain its correctness, its conformity to the rules of the game? . . . For some, yes; when they have done this, they will say, I understand.

"For the majority, no. Almost all are much more exacting; they wish to know not merely whether all the syllogisms of a demonstration are correct, but why they link together in this order rather than another. In so far as to them they seem engendered by caprice and not by an intelligence always conscious of the end to be attained, they do not believe they understand.

"Doubtless they are not themselves just conscious of what they crave, and they could not formulate their desire, but if they do not get satisfaction, they vaguely feel that something is lacking."

The connection of this with our former considerations is easy to understand. For the purpose of teaching—be it oral or written—every part of the argument is brought into its entirely conscious form, corresponding to the simultaneous verifying and "precising" stages which we have described above. Even, in view of further consequences, there is a tendency to increase the number of relay-results. In this way of working, which seems to be the best one of getting a rigorous and clear presentation for the beginner, nothing remains, however, of the synthesis, the importance of which we have underlined in the preceding section. But that synthesis gives the leading thread, without which one would be like the blind man who can walk but would never know in what direction to go.

Those to whom such a synthesis appears "understand mathematics." In the contrary case, there are the two attitudes mentioned by Poincaré. The rather general one is the second one: the student feels that something is lacking, but cannot realize what is wrong; if he does not overcome that difficulty, he will get lost.

In the first case mentioned by Poincaré, the student, not finding any synthetic process, will do without it. Although this allows him to pursue his studies, often for long years, his case is, from a certain point of view, worse than the other one in which at least the existence of some difficulty was understood. On account of the mathematical knowledge more and more required for entrance to several careers, one frequently meets with such a student. I have seen a case in which a candidate, guided by his common sense, knew the right answer to my question, but did not think he was al-

lowed to give it and did not realize that the suggestion of
his subconscious could be very easily translated into a correct and rigorous proof.

Curious instances of this sort are not uncommon among
students in differential and integral calculus. Most often
the question is whether such and such a theorem or formula
is appropriately invoked, whether the conditions for its
application are satisfied or not. Students sometimes indus-
triously investigate that question when common sense indicates the answer to be a practically evident one—and on
the other hand neglect to study it in the case where it is
a delicate one and does deserve a careful examination. Such
remark or analogous ones could be eventually useful in
pedagogy.

*Logic and Intuitive Minds. A Political Aspect of the
Question.* After having spoken of students, let us now deal
with mathematicians themselves, able not only to understand mathematical theories, but also to investigate new
ones. Not only do these differ from ordinary students, but
they also profoundly differ from each other. A capital distinction has been emphasized: some mathematicians are
"intuitive" and others "logical." Poincaré has dealt with
that distinction and so has the German mathematician
Klein. Poincaré's lecture on the subject begins as follows:

"The one sort are above all preoccupied by logic; to read
their works, one is tempted to believe they have advanced
only step by step, after the manner of a Vauban who pushes
on his trenches against the place besieged, leaving nothing
to chance. The other sort are guided by intuition and at
the first stroke, make quick but sometimes precarious con-
quests, like bold cavalrymen of the advance guard."

With Klein, even politics has been introduced into the

question: he asserts[3] that "It would seem as if a strong naive space intuition were an attribute of the Teutonic race, while the critical, purely logical sense is more developed in the Latin and Hebrew races." That such an assertion is not in agreement with facts will appear clearly when we come to examples. It is hardly doubtful that, in stating it, Klein implicitly considers intuition, with its mysterious character, as being superior to the prosaic way of logic (we have already met with such a tendency in Section III) and is evidently happy to claim that superiority for his countrymen. We have heard recently of that special kind of ethnography with Nazism: we see that there was already something of this kind in 1893.

One will find such tendentious interpretations of facts whenever nationalistic passions enter into play. At the beginning of the First World War, one of our greatest scientists and historians of sciences, the physicist Duhem, was misled by them just as Klein had been, only in the opposite sense. In a rather detailed article,[4] he depicts German scientists, especially mathematicians, as lacking intuition or even deliberately setting it aside. It is especially hard to understand how he can characterize in that way Bernhard Riemann who is undoubtedly one of the most typical examples of an intuitive mind. Duhem's assertion of 1915 seems to me as unreasonable as Klein's in 1893. If one or the other were right, the reader will realize by all that precedes that either Frenchmen or Germans would never have made any significant discovery. The only thing for which I should think of reproaching the German mathematical school in that line is a systematic, though hardly

[3] *The Evanston Colloquium*, p. 46.
[4] *Revue des Deux Mondes* (January-February, 1915), p. 657.

defendable and somewhat pedantic claim, chiefly under Klein's influence, that, for certain proofs in analysis and its arithmetical applications, "series" must be used in preference to "integrals." Precisely in those questions, the use of series looks more logical and the use of integrals more intuitive. Perhaps there is again some nationalism in such a tendency, because series are used by the celebrated Weierstrass—a most evident logician—whose reputation and influence have been enormous among German scholars, while, into similar subjects, Cauchy or Hermite introduced integrals[5] (though this was also the case of Riemann).

Poincaré's View of the Distinction. Poincaré, more wisely I think, does not connect the matter with politics. On the contrary, he implicitly shows how doubtful such a connection is: for, in order to illustrate the opposition between the two kinds of mind, he opposes to each other in the first place two Frenchmen and, then, two Germans.

However, after having fully accepted and faithfully followed Poincaré's ideas in Sections I to V, I shall, this time, disagree with him. We have cited the first paragraph of his lecture; let us reproduce the second. It reads as follows:

"The method is not imposed by the matter treated. Though one often says of the first that they are *analysts* and calls the others *geometers*, that does not prevent the one sort from remaining analysts even when they work at geometry, while the others are still geometers even when

---

[5] According to that doctrine, Klein thinks it necessary to modify the proof of a celebrated theorem of Hermite; and even, on reaching a certain point, says "the proof is not yet perfectly simple: something still remains of the ideas of Hermite," this inducing him to a further modification. As a matter of fact, these "simplifications" are superficial ones, and after them just as before them, everything—absolutely everything essential—rests on Hermite's fundamental idea.

they occupy themselves with pure Analysis. It is the very nature of their mind which makes them logicians or intuitionalists, and they cannot lay it aside when they approach a new subject."

What must we think of the comparison between those two paragraphs? Both times, a distinction is made between intuition and logic, but on bases quite different, though somewhat related to each other.[6]

This appears even more clearly in the examples set forth by Poincaré. To Joseph Bertrand, who visibly had a concrete, spatial view of every question, he opposes Hermite whose eyes "seem to shun contact with the world" and who seeks "within, not without, the vision of truth."

That Hermite was not used to thinking in the concrete is certain. He had a kind of positive hatred for geometry and once curiously reproached me with having made a geometrical memoir. As natural, his own memoirs on concrete subjects are very few and not among his most remarkable ones. So, from the second point of view of Poincaré, Hermite ought to be considered as a logical mathematician.

But to call Hermite a logician! Nothing can appear to me as more directly contrary to the truth. Methods always seemed to be born in his mind in some mysterious way. In his lectures at the Sorbonne, which we attended with unfailing enthusiasm, he liked to begin his argument by: "Let us start from the identity . . ." and here he was writing a formula the accuracy of which was certain, but whose origin in his brain and way of discovery he did not explain and we could not guess. This quality of his mind is also most evidently illustrated by his celebrated discovery in the theory of quadratic forms. In that question, two cases

[6] See the remarks at the beginning of this section (p. 101).

are possible in which, as is obvious, things happen quite differently. In the first one, "reduction" has been known since Gauss. Nobody, as it seemed, would have thought of the idea of merely carrying out, in the second case, the very calculations which suited the first one and which apparently, had nothing to do with that second case; it seemed quite absurd that they would, that time, lead to the solution; and yet, by a kind of witchcraft, they do. The mechanism of that extraordinary phenomenon was, some years later, partly explained by a geometrical interpretation (of course, given not by Hermite, but by Klein); but it did not become entirely clear to me before reading Poincaré's conception of it, in one of his early notes.[7] I can hardly imagine a more perfect type of an intuitive mind than Hermite's, if not taking account of the extreme cases which

[7] Poincaré himself, in spite of the inspiration phenomena which we have mentioned, does not make that same impression on me. Reading one of his great discoveries, I should fancy (evidently a delusion) that, however magnificent, one ought to have found it long before, while such memoirs of Hermite as the one referred to in the text arouse in me the idea: "What magnificent results! How could he dream of such a thing?"

There is obviously something subjective in such a judgment. A deduction which will seem to be a logical one for me—that is, congenial to my mind, one which I should be naturally inclined to think of—may appear as intuitive to some other man. Perhaps, almost every mathematician would be a logician according to his own judgment. For instance, I have been asked by what kind of guessing I thought of the device of the "finite part of infinite integral," which I have used for the integration of partial differential equations. Certainly, considering it in itself, it looks typically like "thinking aside." But, in fact, for a long while my mind refused to conceive that idea until positively compelled to. I was led to it step by step as the mathematical reader will easily verify if he takes the trouble to consult my researches on the subject, especially my *Recherches sur les Solutions Fondamentales et l'Intégration des Équations Linéaires aux Dérivées Partielles*, 2nd Memoir, especially pp. 121 ff. (Annales scientifiques de l'Ecole Normale Supérieure, Vol. XXII₃, 1905). I could not avoid it any more than the prisoner in Poe's tale *The Pit and the Pendulum* could avoid the hole at the center of his cell.

will be mentioned in the next section. Hermite's example undoubtedly shows that the two definitions of intuition and logic given by Poincaré do not agree or do not necessarily agree, which Poincaré finally admits to a certain extent on account of that case.

The two German mathematicians whom Poincaré compares are Weierstrass and Riemann. That, as he concludes, Riemann is typically intuitive and Weierstrass typically logical is beyond contestation. But as to the latter, Poincaré says "You may leaf through all his books without finding a figure." It strikes me that there happens to be there an error of fact.[8] It is true that *almost* no memoir of Weierstrass implied any figure: there is only one exception; but there is one, and this exception occurs in one of his most masterly and clear-cut works, one giving the most complete impression of perfection: I mean his fundamental method in the calculus of variations. Weierstrass draws a simple diagram[8a] and, after that initial step is taken, everything goes on in the profoundly logical way which is undoubtedly his characteristic, so that, by merely looking at that diagram, anyone sufficiently acquainted with mathematical methods could have rebuilt the whole argument. But of course there was an initial intuition, that of constructing the diagram. This was the more difficult and the more evidently an act of genius because it meant breaking from the general methods which had continued to become more and more successful after the invention of infinitesi-

[8] An error for which, however, Poincaré is not to be reproached (see next footnote).

[8a] Whether Weierstrass himself actually drew the diagram (or simply described it in words) cannot be said because he did not develop his method elsewhere than in his oral lectures. That method remained unknown for years, except to his former students.

mal calculus, which had been beautifully successful in the
hands of Lagrange for obtaining the first stage of the
solution, though not enabling anybody to complete it correctly. Weierstrass showed that abandoning these methods
and operating directly was the right way for that.

In reality, as we see, this is an undeniable case of the
general fact of logic following an initial intuition.

Application of Our Previous Data. We are thus compelled to admit that there is not a single definition of intuition *vs.* logic, but there are at least two different ones.
Now, for elucidating this, why should we not make use of
what we have found in our former analysis of the phenomena?

Summing up the results of that analysis, let us remember that every mental work and especially the work of
discovery implies the cooperation of the unconscious, be
it the superficial or (fairly often) the more or less remote
one; that, inside of that unconscious (resulting from a preliminary conscious work), there is that starting of ideas
which Poincaré has compared to a projection of atoms and
which can be more or less scattered; that concrete representations are generally used by the mind for the maintenance
and synthesis of combinations.

This carries, in the first place, the consequence that,
strictly speaking, there is hardly any completely logical
discovery. Some intervention of intuition issuing from the
unconscious is necessary at least to initiate the logical
work.

With this reservation, we immediately see that the processes such as those described above can behave differently
in different minds.

(A) More or Less Depth in the Unconscious. As we know

that there must be several layers in the unconscious, some
quite near consciousness while some may lie more and more
remote, it is clear that the levels at which ideas meet and
combine may be deeper or, on the contrary, more superficial; and it is not unreasonable to admit that there is a
usual behavior of every single mind from that point of
view.

It is quite natural to speak of a more intuitive mind if
the zone where ideas are combined is deeper, and of a
logical one if that zone is rather superficial. This manner
of facing the distinction is the one I should believe to be
the most important.

If that zone is deeper, there will be more difficulty in
bringing the result to the knowledge of consciousness and
it is likely to happen that the mind will have a tendency
to do so only for what is strictly necessary. I should think
this to be the case with Hermite, who certainly did not omit
anything strictly essential in the results of his reflections,
so that his methods were quite correct and rigorous, but
without letting any trace remain of the way in which he
had been led to them.

The contrary may happen: some minds may be such that
ideas elaborated in the depth of the unconscious are nevertheless integrally brought to the light of consciousness. I
should fancy that as happening with Poincaré, whose ideas,
inspired as they may have been by farsighted intuitions,
generally seemed to follow a quite natural way. One sees
that there can be apparent logicians, who are logical in the
enunciation of their ideas, after having been intuitive in
their discovery.[9]

[9] Generally speaking, as some authors observe (see Meyerson *Du
Cheminement de la Pensée*, Vol. 1, cited in Delacroix *L'Invention et le*

(B) More or Less Narrowly Directed Thought. In the second place, we have seen that the projection of Poincaré's atoms—the starting of ideas, to use a less metaphorical language—can be more or less scattered. This is another reason why we can have the sensation of an intuitive mind (which will happen if there is much scattering) or (in the contrary case) of a logical mind; and the second reason can, at least a priori, be without any connection with the first one: the direction of thought may be narrower or wider, be it at one level of unconsciousness or at another. A priori, we do not know whether there is not a connection between these two kinds of "intuitive tendencies"; but in fact, an example (see below the case of Galois) will show us independence.

(C) Different Auxiliary Representations. We have seen how differently scientists behave as to the way in which their thought is helped by mental pictures or other concrete representations: differences can bear either on the nature of representations or on the way they influence the work of the mind. It is evident that some of these kinds of representations may give the thought a rather logical course, some others a rather intuitive one. But this side of the question is much less accessible to study, precisely because phenomena are not always comparable in different minds.

We can understand the use of geometrical images in intuition with the help of reference to Section II (especially p. 24 and the footnote of p. 23) and Section VI (p. 65). A most evident fact of observation is that a quite perfect organization and synthesis of usual sensations occurs in

Genie, p. 480), there is often a great difference between the discovery of an idea and its enunciation.

our earliest childhood, taking place in the very deep layers of our unconscious, and consequently with very great rapidity (the time required lying far below the reach of our measuring methods). That such a process should be especially adapted to intuition, considered from our point of view (A), is quite natural.

It would have been most interesting to get the auto-observations of Hermite, who, though a highly intuitive mind, seems to be so completely distant from geometrical and, generally speaking, concrete considerations.

Other Differences in Mathematical Minds. The above question is the only one which has been examined so far, concerning different kinds of mathematical minds; but, of course, there is no doubt that mathematicians can differ from each other from various other points of view.

For instance, there exists a theory, the theory of groups, the importance of which, in our science, grew increasingly for more than one century, especially since the work of Sophus Lie at the end of the nineteenth century. Some mathematicians, especially contemporary ones, have improved it by most beautiful discoveries. Some others—I confess that I belong to the latter category—though being eventually able to use it for simple applications, feel insuperable difficulty in mastering more than a rather elementary and superficial knowledge of it. Psychological reasons for that difference, which seems to me incontestable, would be interesting to find.

VIII. PARADOXICAL CASES OF INTUITION

If, in some exceptionally intuitive minds, ideas may evolve and combine in still deeper unconscious layers than in the above-mentioned cases, then even important links of the deduction may remain unknown to the thinker himself who has found them. The history of science offers some remarkable examples.

Fermat (1601-1661). Pierre de Fermat was a magistrate, a counselor at the Parliament of Toulouse. It was a time when life was less complicated than nowadays, and the requirements of his duties apparently did not hamper him in his mathematical researches, which were considerable. Besides having participated in the origins of infinitesimal calculus and even in the creation of calculus of probabilities, he dealt actively with arithmetical questions. Among the ancient mathematicians whose works were in his possession, he owned a translation of the work of Diophantes, a Greek author who had dealt with such arithmetical subjects. Now, at Fermat's death, his copy of Diophantes' work was found to bear in the margin the following observation (in Latin):

"I have proved that the relation $x^m + y^m = z^m$ is impossible in integral numbers (x, y, z different from 0; m greater than 2); but the margin does not leave me room enough to inscribe the proof."

Three centuries have elapsed since then, and that proof which Fermat could have written in the margin had the latter been a little broader, is still sought for. However, Fermat does not seem to have been mistaken, for partial

proofs have been found, viz., proofs for some extended classes of values of the exponent m: for instance, the proof has been obtained for every *m* not greater than 100. But the work—an immense one—which made it possible to get these partial results could not be accomplished by direct arithmetical considerations:[1] it required the help of some important algebraic theories of which no knowledge existed in the time of Fermat *and no conception appears in his writings.* After several fundamental principles of algebra had been laid down during the eighteenth century and at the beginning of the nineteenth, the German mathematician Kummer, in order to attack that question of the "last theorem of Fermat," was obliged to introduce a new and audacious conception, the "ideals," a grand idea which entirely revolutionized algebra. As we just said, even that powerful tool given to mathematical thought allows, as yet, only a partial proof of the mysterious theorem.

Riemann (1826-1866). Bernhard Riemann, whose extraordinary intuitive power we have already mentioned, has especially renovated our knowledge of the distribution of prime numbers, also one of the most mysterious questions in mathematics.[2] He has taught us to deduce results

[1] The use of considerations of that kind has been attempted by the most prominent masters—beginning with Abel—during the last two centuries. Every significant gain which can be obtained in that direction seems to have been reached, and those gains are quite limited ones. The French Academy of Sciences in Paris yearly receives several papers on that subject, most of which are absurd, while a few reproduce known results of Abel or others.

[2] Both those instances concerning Fermat and Riemann relate to arithmetic. Indeed, arithmetic, which is the first study in elementary teaching, is one of the most difficult, if not the most difficult branch of mathematics, when one tries to penetrate it more deeply. Essential gains are generally obtained, as happens in our examples, on an arithmetical question by reconducting it to higher algebra or to the infinitesimal calculus.

It must be observed that the example of this discovery of Riemann

in that line from considerations borrowed from the integral calculus: more precisely, from the study of a certain quantity, a function of a variable s which may assume not only real, but also imaginary values. He proved some important properties of that function, but pointed out several as important ones without giving the proof. At the death of Riemann, a note was found among his papers, saying "These properties of $\zeta(s)$ (the function in question) are deduced from an expression of it which, however, I did not succeed in simplifying enough to publish it."

We still have not the slightest idea of what the expression could be. As to the properties he simply enunciated, some thirty years elapsed before I was able to prove all of them but one. The question concerning that last one remains unsolved as yet, though, by an immense labor pursued throughout this last half century, some highly interesting discoveries in that direction have been achieved. It seems more and more probable, but still not at all certain, that the "Riemann hypothesis" is true. Of course, all these complements could be brought to Riemann's publication only by the help of facts which were completely unknown in his time; and, for one of the properties enunciated by him, it is hardly conceivable how he can have found it without using some of these general principles, no mention of which is made in his paper.

Galois (1811-1831). Most striking is the personality of Evariste Galois whose tragic life, abruptly ended in his

again illustrates the difference between two aspects of intuition which Poincaré believed to be identical. In general, Riemann's intuition, as Poincaré observes, is highly geometrical; but this is not the case for his memoir on prime numbers, the one in which that intuition is the most powerful and mysterious: in that memoir, there is no important role of geometrical elements.

early youth, brought to science one of the most capital monuments we know of. Galois' passionate nature was captivated by mathematical science from the moment he became acquainted with Legendre's geometry. However, he was violently dominated by another overpowering feeling, enthusiastic devotion to republican and liberal ideas, for which he fought in a passionate and sometimes very imprudent way. Nevertheless, the death he met with at the age of twenty did not occur in that struggle, but in an absurd duel.

Galois spent the night before that duel in revising his notes on his discoveries. First, the manuscript which had been rejected by the Academy of Sciences as being unintelligible (one may not wonder that such highly intuitive minds are very obscure) ; then, in a letter directed to a friend, scanty and hurried mention of other beautiful views, with the same words hastily and repeatedly inscribed in the margin "I have no time." Indeed, few hours remained to him before going where death awaited him.

All those profound ideas were at first forgotten and it was only after fifteen years that, with admiration, scientists became aware of the memoir which the Academy had rejected. It signifies a total transformation of higher algebra, projecting a full light on what had been only glimpsed thus far by the greatest mathematicians, and, at the same time, connecting that algebraic problem with others in quite different branches of science.

But what especially belongs to our subject is one point in the letter written by Galois to his friend and enunciating a theorem on the "periods" of a certain kind of integrals. Now, this theorem, which is clear for us, could not have been understood by scientists living at the time of Galois:

these "periods" had no meaning in the state of science of
that day; they acquired one only by means of some principles in the theory of functions, today classical, but which
were not found before something like a quarter of a century after the death of Galois. It must be admitted, therefore: (1) that Galois must have conceived these principles
in some way; (2) that they must have been unconscious
in his mind, since he makes no allusion to them, though
they by themselves represent a significant discovery.

The case of Galois deserves some attention in connection
with our former distinction. In some ways he reminds us of
Hermite. He is, like him, a thoroughly analytical mathematician, though he came to his first and enthusiastic
vision of science by the geometry of Legendre. One of his
early essays while a schoolboy was of a geometrical nature,
but it was the only one. A curious thing is that Galois'
teacher in mathematics in the high school, Mr. Richard,
who had the merit of discovering at once his extraordinary
abilities, was also, fifteen years later, the teacher of Hermite; this, however, cannot be regarded otherwise than as
a mere coincidence, since the genius of such men is evidently
a gift of nature, independent of any teaching.

On the other hand, Galois, who was evidently highly intuitive according to our definition (A), does not appear as
such in terms of the definition (B). In the proof of the
general theorem which affords a definitive solution to the
main problem of algebra, there is no trace of "scattered
ideas," no combination of apparently heterogeneous principles: his thought is, so to speak, an intensive and not an
extensive one; and I should be inclined to say as much of
the discoveries contained in his posthumous letter (the
letter written during the night just before his fatal duel),

though the stream of thought cannot be so surely characterized on such a sequel of simply and briefly enunciated results. This does not exclude the occasional possibility of a connection between the aspects (A) and (B) of intuition; but in Galois' case, they appear to be independent of each other.

From the second point of view, it is clear that Galois profoundly differs from Hermite, whose discovery concerning quadratic forms is a typical example of "thinking aside."

A Case in the Work of Poincaré. It seems to have been unnoticed that something similar occurs in Poincaré's *Méthodes Nouvelles de la Mécanique Celeste.* In his Volume III (see p. 261), he has to deal with the calculus of variations and he uses a sufficient condition for a minimum, equivalent to the one which results from Weierstrass's method (see above, p. 111). But he does not give a proof of that condition: he speaks of it as a known fact. Now, as we have said, Weierstrass's method was not published at the time when that volume of the *Méthodes Nouvelles* was written. Moreover, he does not make any mention of Weierstrass's discovery, which he should have necessarily done if he had received any private communication of it. Above all, it must be added that the condition is formulated in a form slightly different (though basically equivalent) from the one which is classically known as resulting from Weierstrass's method. Must we think that Weierstrass's argument or an analogous one was found by Poincaré and remained unconscious in his mind?[3]

---

[3] The case appears a still stranger one if we notice that at the same page (p. 261) of his third volume, just a few lines before, Poincaré writes: "Cette recherche se rattache à la difficile question de la variation seconde."

Historical Comparisons. In such cases, we must admit that some parts of the mental process develop so deeply in the unconscious that some parts of it, even important ones, remain hidden from our conscious self. We come very near the phenomena of dual personality such as were observed by psychologists of the nineteenth century.

Even intermediaries seem to have existed between the two kinds of phenomena. I think of Socrates' ideas being suggested to him by a familiar demon or also of the nymph Egeria whom Numa Pompilius used to consult frequently.

An analogous example can possibly be spoken of in the mathematical field. It is Cardan, who is not only the inventor of a well-known joint which is an essential part of automobiles, but who has also fundamentally transformed mathematical science by the invention of imaginaries. Let us recall what an imaginary quantity is. The rules of algebra show that the square of any number, whether positive or negative, is a positive number: therefore, to speak of the square root of a negative number is mere absurdity. Now, Cardan deliberately commits that absurdity and begins to calculate on such "imaginary" quantities.

One would describe this as pure madness; and yet the whole development of algebra and analysis would have been

Now, in Weierstrass's theory—that is, in our present view of the calculus of variations—there is no question of the second variation, which is fully left out of consideration.

Therefore, there is a curious contradiction in that page of the *Méthodes Nouvelles*. The allusion to the "variation seconde" is that of a man having no idea of the new theory. On the contrary, Poincaré proves to have been fully aware of it when he enunciated his condition (A) (his form of Weierstrass's condition): nobody thought of anything of that kind in the older ideas on the subject; one only knew of the classic (but less adequate) "Legendre condition."

Should one think of the case of Poincaré as of a kind of dual personality?

impossible without that fundament—which, of course, was, in the nineteenth century, established on solid and rigorous bases. It has been written that the shortest and best way between two truths of the real domain often passes through the imaginary one.

We have mentioned Cardan's case with Socrates' and Numa Pompilius', because he too is reported by some of his biographers to have received suggestions from a mysterious voice at certain periods of his life. However, testimonies on that point do not agree at least in details.

IX. THE GENERAL DIRECTION
OF RESEARCH

BEFORE trying to discover anything or to solve a determinate problem, there arises the question: what shall we try to discover? What problem shall we try to solve?

Two Conceptions of Invention. Claparède, in his introductory lecture before the above-mentioned meeting at the Centre de Synthèse, observes that there are two kinds of invention: one consists, a goal being given, in finding the means to reach it, so that the mind goes from the goal to the means, from the question to the solution; the other consists, on the contrary, in discovering a fact, then imagining what it could be useful for, so that, this time, mind goes from the means to the goal; the answer appears to us before the question.

Now, paradoxical as it seems, that second kind of invention is the more general one and becomes more and more so as science advances. Practical application is found by not looking for it, and one can say that the whole progress of civilization rests on that principle. When the Greeks, some four centuries B.C., considered the ellipse—i.e., the curve generated by the points M in a plane such that the sum $MF + MF'$ of their distances from two given points F, F′ be a constant—and found many remarkable properties of it, they did not think and could not think of any possible use for such discoveries. However, without these studies, Kepler could not have discovered, two thousand years later, the laws of motion of planets, and Newton could not have discovered universal attraction.

Even results which are more strictly practical obey the same rule. Balloons, in earlier days, were filled with hydrogen or lighting gas, which constituted a serious danger of fire. At the present time, we are able to fill balloons with incombustible gas. This progress has been possible for two reasons: in the first place, because one has succeeded in knowing which substances exist in the atmosphere of the sun and which do not; secondly, because research was started, by Lord Rayleigh and Ramsay among others, in order to determine the density of nitrogen exactly to the 1/10,000, instead of the precision of 1/1,000 which was known previously.

Both are subjects which were investigated and elucidated without foreseeing any possible applications.

We must add, however, that, conversely, application is useful and eventually essential to theory by the very fact that it opens new questions for the latter. One could say that application's constant relation to theory is the same as that of the leaf to the tree: one supports the other, but the former feeds the latter. Not to mention several important physical examples, the first mathematical foundation in Greek science, geometry, was suggested by practical necessity, as can be seen by its very name, which means "land-measuring."

But this example is exceptional in the sense that practical questions are most often solved by means of existing theories: practical applications of purely scientific discoveries, important as they may be, are generally remote in time (though, in recent years, this delay may be considerably shortened, as happened in the case of radio telegraphy, which occurred a few years after the discovery of Hertzian waves). It seldom happens that important mathematical researches are *directly* undertaken in view of a given practical use: they are inspired by the desire which is the common motive of every scientific work, the desire to know and to understand. Therefore, between the two kinds of invention we have just distinguished from each other, mathematicians are accustomed only to the second one.

The Choice of Subjects. But setting aside practical applications, which generally, if they exist, lie far away in time, mathematical discoveries can be more or less rich in theoretical consequences. Even these are most often unknown to us, as fully unknown as incombustible balloons were to the men who, for the first time, discovered the chemical composition of the atmosphere of the sun.

Then, how are we to select subjects of research? This delicate choice is one of the most important things in research; according to it we form, generally in a reliable manner, our judgment of the value of a scientist.

Upon it we base even our judgment of research students. Students have often consulted me for subjects of research; when asked for such guidance, I have given it willingly, but I must confess that—provisionally, of course—I have been inclined to classify the man as second rate. In a different field, such was the opinion of our great Indianist Sylvain Levi, who told me that, on being asked such a question, he was tempted to reply: Now, my young friend, you have attended our courses for, say, three or four years and you have never perceived that there is something wanting further investigation?

But how is that important and difficult choice to be directed? The answer is hardly doubtful: it is the same which Poincaré gave us concerning the means of discovery,

the same for the "drive" as for the "mechanism." The guide
we must confide in is that sense of scientific beauty, that
special esthetic sensibility, the importance of which he has
pointed out.

As Renan also curiously notices,[1] there is a scientific
taste just as there is a literary or artistic one; and that
taste, according to individuals, may be more or less sure.

Concerning the fruitfulness of the future result, about
which, strictly speaking, we most often do not know anything in advance, that sense of beauty can inform us and
I cannot see anything else allowing us to foresee. At least,
contesting that would seem to me to be a mere question of
words. Without knowing anything further, we *feel* that
such a direction of investigation is worth following; we
feel that the question *in itself* deserves interest, that its
solution will be of some value for science, whether it permits
further applications or not. Everybody is free to call or
not to call that a feeling of beauty. This is undoubtedly
the way the Greek geometers thought when they investigated the ellipse, because there is no other conceivable way.

As to applications, though completely unforeseen, they
do most often arise later on, if our original feeling has
been a right one. I shall report one or two personal instances, apologizing for that repeated intervention of my
own example on which, of course, I am especially informed.

When I presented my doctor's thesis for examination,
Hermite observed that it would be most useful to find applications. At that time, I had none available. Now, between the time my manuscript was handed in and the day
when the thesis was sustained, I became aware of an important question (the one we have spoken of at p. 118 in con-

---

[1] *L'Avenir de la Science*, p. 115.

nection with Riemann) which had been proposed by the
French Academy of Sciences as a prize subject; and precisely, the results in my thesis gave the solution of that
question. I had been uniquely led by my feeling of the interest of the problem and it led me in the right way.

A few years later, having, in a further study of the same
kind of questions, obtained a very simple result[2] which
seemed to me an elegant one, I communicated it to my
friend, the physicist Duhem. He asked to what it applied.
When I answered that so far I had not thought of that,
Duhem, who was a remarkable artist as well as a prominent physicist, compared me to a painter who would begin
by painting a landscape without leaving his studio and
only then start on a walk to find in nature some landscape
suiting his picture. This argument seemed to be correct,
but, as a matter of fact, I was right in not worrying about
applications: they did come afterwards.

Some years before (1893), I had been attracted by a
question in algebra (on determinants). When solving it, I
had no suspicion of any definite use it might have, only
feeling that it deserved interest; then in 1900 appeared
Fredholm's theory,[3] for which the result obtained in 1893
happens to be essential.

Most surprising—I should say bewildering—facts of
that kind are connected with the extraordinary march of
contemporary physics. In 1913, Elie Cartan, one of the
first among French mathematicians, thought of a remarkable class of analytic and geometric transformations in

---

[2] For technicians, the "composition theorem."
[3] This is the theory which, as said in Section IV, I failed to discover.
It has been a consolation for my self-esteem to have brought a necessary
link to Fredholm's arguments.

relation to the theory of groups. No reason was seen, at that time, for special consideration of those transformations except just their esthetic character. Then, some fifteen years later, experiments revealed to physicists some extraordinary phenomena concerning electrons, which they could only understand by the help of Cartan's ideas of 1913.

But hardly any more typical instance in that line can be set forth than modern functional calculus. When Jean Bernoulli, in the eighteenth century, asked for the curve along which a small heavy body would go down from a point A to a point B in the shortest possible time, he was necessarily tempted by the beauty of that problem, so different from what had been attacked hitherto though evidently offering an analogy with those already treated by infinitesimal calculus. That beauty alone could tempt him. The consequences which "calculus of variations"—i.e., the theory of problems of that kind—would carry for the improvement of mechanics, at the end of the eighteenth century and the beginning of the nineteenth, could not be suspected in his time.

Much more surprising is the fate of the extension given to that initial conception in the last part of the nineteenth century, chiefly under the powerful impulse of Volterra. Why was the great Italian geometer led to operate on functions as infinitesimal calculus had operated on numbers, that is to consider a function as a continuously variable element? Only because he realized that this was a harmonious way of completing the architecture of the mathematical building, just as the architect sees that the building will be better poised by the addition of a new wing. One could already imagine that, as explained in Section III, such a harmonious creation could be of help for solving problems concerning functions considered in the previous fashion; but that "functionals," as we called the new conception, could be in direct relation with reality could not be thought of otherwise than as mere absurdity. Functionals seemed to be an essentially and completely abstract creation of mathematicians.

Now, precisely the absurd has happened. Hardly intelligible and conceivable as it seems, in the ideas of contemporary physicists (in the recent theory of "wave mechanics"), the new notion, the treatment of which is accessible only to students already familiar with very advanced calculus, is absolutely necessary for the mathematical representation of any physical phenomenon. Any observable element, such as a pressure, a speed, etc., which one used to define by a number, can no longer be considered as such, but is mathematically represented by a functional!

These examples are a sufficient answer to Wallas's doubt on the value of the sense of beauty as a "drive" for discovery. On the contrary, in our mathematical field, it seems to be almost the only useful one.

We again see how direction in thought implies affective elements, such being especially the case as concerns that continuity of attention, that faithfulness of the mind to its object, the importance of which we have already pointed out in Section IV.[4]

In the present stage, as in inspiration, choice is directed by the sense of beauty; but, this time we refer to it con-

[4] In a question of inversive geometry (see Section IV), I had underestimated the beauty of the question and failed to devote to it a sufficient continuity of attention.

sciously, while it works in the unconscious to give us inspiration.

Direction of Inventive Work and Desire of Originality.
May other reasons influence the direction of research?

As Dr. de Saussure rightly observes, the intervention of emotional causes is often possible (he gives me typical examples in the life of Freud, the creator of psychoanalysis). However, this chances to be less the case as concerns mathematics, on account of the abstract character of that science where, according to Bertrand Russell's celebrated word: "We never know what we are talking about, nor whether what we are saying is true."

Dr. de Saussure has also raised the question whether creative workers could not be moved by a less laudable kind of passion, deriving from human vanity: the desire of doing something unlike others.

It seems to me that something of this kind is possible in art or literature. More exactly, any question of vanity being set aside, not being similar to others is a requisite which the artist (or similarly, the literary man) must consider in itself. Of course, this observation does not apply to the really great ones: for instance, we have seen by Mozart's letter (p. 17) that he did not have to think of being original. But did not such a necessity have its part in the founding of some schools of painters; or in the works where some literary men try to interpret in a paradoxical way the actions or psychology of known personalities? One may ask that question.

We might see some connection between this and a certain number of known cases where poets or other artists have produced works in abnormal states (for instance,

Coleridge in a state of laudanum-sleep). Wallas,[5] who reports such examples, considers that a slight degree of "dissociation of mind" may be useful for the artist "who wishes to break with his own habits of thought and vision and those of his school." Also, it is not unusual to hear of poetical works composed in dreams, while we have seen that this is very rare, if not doubtful, in mathematical production.

The case of the scientist who, as has been said in the beginning, is a servant and not a master, is indeed a different one. Any result, the solution of any problem he knows of, makes new problems arise before him. As a matter of fact, I can hardly think of more than two or three memoirs which I would describe as bizarre rather than as truly original.

Nevertheless, the scientist may be and often is discouraged from studying such and such a problem not by the knowledge that it has been solved, but by the fear that it has been solved without his knowing it, a fact which would render his work useless; or—and this is more disinterested on his part—it is natural for him to be attracted by a question not devoid of importance in itself on account of its having been overlooked until then. Such has often been my case; I even add that, after having started a certain set of questions and seeing that several other authors had begun to follow that same line, I happened to drop it and investigate something else. I have been told by physicists that some of the prominent men in contemporary physics often act in the same way.

[5] *The Art of Thought*, pp. 206-210. That very great masters do not need to strive for originality is interpreted by Wallas in saying that, for them, "at the moment of production, a harmony is attained between an intense activity of the whole nervous system, higher and lower alike, and the conscious will."

Also, we see clearly how mistaken Souriau was, certainly because he did not direct inquiries among scholars, when he spoke of them as being desirous of some great discovery "in order to attract public attention" or, "to get an agreeable and independent appointment." We can admit that motives of that kind occasionally influence the life of some of us—when tempted to slacken our work—as did the classic word: "Thou sleepest, Brutus." It is possible that Ampère was doing more than answering Julie Ampère's urgent anxieties when he wrote her that publishing one of his discoveries would be a good means of securing a professorship in a lycée. But it was not that which made him discover; nor could I conceive of a scientific man who would be led to discover chiefly in that way. Scholars with minds of that sort could get only poor results; whether it be in the choice of questions or in their treatment, a man without some love of science could not be successful, because he would be unable to choose.[6]

FINAL REMARKS

I have tried to report and interpret observations, personal or gathered from other scholars engaged in the work of invention. There remain many other important aspects

[6] Points of view substantially analogous to ours in this section are the object of G. H. Hardy's recent and suggestive little book *A Mathematician's Apology*. Although he does not get to a complete definition of the beauty—or, as he calls it, "seriousness"—of a mathematical question or result, on which, of course, esthetic feeling must intervene, he gives a very delicate and acute analysis of the conditions suitable for the approach to such a definition.

He also discusses the motives which may influence the desire of research. He sees three chiefly important ones, the first of them being, of course, the desire to know the truth. For the reason given in the text, I should insist more than he does on the predominant character and even necessity of that first one.

of the subject, especially "objective" ones, which we have already had occasion to mention. Such are the possible relations between inventive thought and bodily phenomena. Ideas more or less analogous to those of Gall would deserve to be pursued. But how could this be done? It would require somebody more qualified than I am—better acquainted with the physiology of the brain. However, here we meet with the difficulty which we mentioned in the beginning; while mathematicians have not sufficient knowledge of neurology, neurologists cannot be expected to penetrate deeply (as would be necessary) into mathematical studies. Will it ever happen that mathematicians will know enough of that subject of the physiology of the brain and that neurophysiologists know enough of mathematical discovery for efficient cooperation to be possible?

Similarly, I could not venture to say anything about the social and historical influences which surely act on invention as they do on everything else. I do not know much about the mechanism of that influence; and the question is whether anybody does. Such attempts as Taine's in his *Philosophie de l'Art*, although their principle bears the mark of genius, are certainly premature and very hypothetical in their conclusions. Indeed, the difficulties of such an attempt are obvious: not only is there the fact that no experiment is possible, but even (genius apart) men with notable inventive powers are too rare to allow an extensive application of comparative methods, so that Taine's question and our own are among the most difficult even between those of an historical nature. Social influences govern mathematical development in the same unconscious and rather mysterious way as they do literary or artistic ones. There may certainly be something right in Klein's idea of an intervention of Galton's heredity theories as concerns intuitive and logical qualities of the mind (and the same might be said of mathematical aptitude in general and of the way various minds use concrete representations) ; but it is quite unlikely that things are as simple as was imagined by the school of Taine. It is certainly not a fortuitous thing that, at the time of the Renaissance and especially in Italy, there were so many extraordinary men of every kind, a Benvenuto Cellini and a Leonardo da Vinci as well as a Galilei; but it is more doubtful that the reasons for such a marvellous phenomenon are those supposed by Taine.[1]

Things may eventually be clearer when, instead of general cases, we consider some individual ones. Saying that, I think of the case of Cardan, who lived at that same time and who, in fact, was one of the most extraordinary characters of that extraordinary time. It could be naturally expected that that discovery of imaginaries which seems nearer to madness than to logic and which, in fact, has illuminated the whole mathematical science, would come from such a man whose adventurous life was not always commendable from the moral point of view, and who from childhood suffered from fantastic hallucinations to such an extent that he was chosen by Lombroso as a typical example in the chapter "Genius and Insanity" of his book on *The Man of Genius*.

If we do not recur to such special cases, the exceptional

[1] Is the similitude in the evolution of ideas among Greek philosophers and among thinkers of the Middle Ages, as concerns words and wordless thought, more than a fortuitous coincidence, and would it mean a general law in the evolution of thought? Of course, one should not dare to make a positive assertion on the basis of only two instances. If proved, the fact would be a rather significant one. A study on that question in Arabian philosophy (especially in the Spanish period) or in Asiatic philosophies could be of interest.

character of the phenomena which we have considered creates an obstacle to study as soon as one leaves aside the data supplied by introspection. But, on the other hand, one may wonder whether such processes cannot help us to elucidate those which go on in other psychological realms: for instance, as we have seen, those examined in Section VI may have some features in common with the role of images as considered by Taine or with problems raised by the Gestalt theory. In conformity with a rule which seems applicable to every science of observation (that it even applies in mathematics appears from the fact noticed in Section VIII, p. 117 footnote), it is the exceptional phenomenon which is likely to explain the usual one; and, consequently, whatever we can observe that has to do with invention or even, as in this study, this or that kind of invention, is capable of throwing light on psychology in general.

APPENDIX I

AN INQUIRY INTO THE WORKING METHODS OF MATHEMATICIANS

Translated from *L'Enseignement Mathématique,*
Vol. IV, 1902 and Vol. VI, 1904

———

1. At what time, as well as you can remember, and under what circumstances did you begin to be interested in mathematical sciences? *Have you inherited your liking for mathematical sciences? Were any of your immediate ancestors or members of your family (brothers, sisters, uncles, cousins, etc.) particularly good at mathematics? Was their influence or example to any extent responsible for your propensity for mathematics?

2. Toward what branches of mathematical science did you feel especially attracted?

3. Are you more interested in mathematical science per se or in its applications to natural phenomena?

4. Have you a distinct recollection of your manner of working while you were pursuing your studies, when the goal was rather to assimilate the results of others than to indulge in personal research? Have you any interesting information to offer on that point?

5. After having completed the regular course of mathematical studies (which, for instance, corresponds to the program of the Licence mathematique or of two Licences[1] or of the Aggregation,[2] in what direction did you consider it expedient to continue your studies? Did you endeavor, in the first place, to obtain a general and extensive knowledge of several parts of science before writing or publishing anything of consequence? Did you, on the contrary, at first try to penetrate rather deeply into a special subject, study-

* Items preceded by an asterisk appeared in Vol. VI.
[1] French grade corresponding to B.A. and M.A. degrees.
[2] A grade, or rather a competition, required for teaching in high schools.

ing almost exclusively what was strictly requisite for that purpose, and only afterwards extending your studies little by little? If you have used other methods, can you indicate them briefly? Which one do you prefer?

6. Among the truths which you have discovered, have you attempted to determine the genesis of those you consider the most valuable?

7. What, in your estimation, is the role played by chance or inspiration in mathematical discoveries? Is this role always as great as it appears to be?

8. Have you noticed that, occasionally, discoveries or solutions on a subject entirely foreign to the one you are dealing with occur to you and that these relate to previous unsuccessful research efforts of yours?

*8b. Have you ever worked in your sleep or have you found in dreams the answers to problems? Or, when you waken in the morning, do solutions which you had vainly sought the night before, or even days before, or quite unexpected discoveries, present themselves ready-made to your mind?

9. Would you say that your principal discoveries have been the result of deliberate endeavor in a definite direction, or have they arisen, so to speak, spontaneously in your mind?

10. When you have arrived at a conclusion about something you are investigating with a view to the publication of your findings, do you immediately write down the part of your work to which that discovery applies; or do you let your conclusions accumulate in the form of notes and begin the redaction of the work only when its contents are important enough?

11. Generally speaking, how much importance do you attach to reading for mathematical research? What advice in this respect would you give to a young mathematician who has had the usual classical education?

12. Before beginning a piece of research work, do you first attempt to assimilate what has already been written on that subject?

13. Or do you prefer to leave your mind free to work unbiased and do you only afterwards verify by reading about the subject

so as to ascertain just what is your personal contribution to the conclusions reached?

14. When you take up a question, do you try to make as general a study as possible of the more or less specific problems which occur to you? Do you usually prefer, first to study special cases or a more inclusive one, and then to generalize progressively?

15. As far as method is concerned, do you make any distinction between invention and redacting?

16. Does it seem to you that your habits of work are appreciably the same as they were before you had completed your studies?

17. In your principal research studies, have you followed the same line of thought steadily and uninterruptedly to the end, or have you laid it aside at times and subsequently taken it up again?

18. What is, in your opinion, the minimum number of hours during the day, the week, or the year, which a mathematician who has other demands on his time should devote to mathematics so as to study profitably certain branches of these same mathematics? Do you believe that one should, if one can, study a little every day, say for one hour at the very least?

19. Do artistic and literary occupations, especially those of music and poetry, seem to you likely to hamper mathematical invention, or do you think they help it by giving the mind temporary rest?

19a. What are your favorite hobbies, pursuits, or chief interests, aside from mathematics, or in your leisure time—b. Do metaphysical, ethical, or religious questions attract or repel you?

20. If you are absorbed by professional duties, how do you fit these in with your personal studies?

21. What counsels, in brief, would you offer to a young man studying mathematics? *b. to a young mathematician who has finished the usual course of study and desires to follow a scientific career?

QUESTIONS ABOUT DAILY HABITS

22. Do you believe that it is beneficial to a mathematician to observe a few special rules of hygiene such as diet, regular meals, time for rest, etc.?

23. What do you consider the normal amount of sleep necessary?

24. Would you say that a mathematician's work should be interrupted by other occupations or by physical exercises which are suited to the individual's age and strength?

25. Or, on the contrary, do you think one should devote the whole day to one's work and not allow anything to interfere with it; and, when it is finished, take several days of complete rest? *b. Do you experience definite periods of inspiration and enthusiasm succeeded by periods of depression and incapacity for work? c. Have you noticed whether these intervals alternate regularly and, if so, how many days, approximately, does the period of activity last and also the period of inertia? d. Do physical or meteorological conditions (i.e., temperature, light, darkness, the season of the year, etc.) exert an appreciable influence on your ability to work?

26. What physical exercises do you do, or have you done as relaxation from mental work? Which do you prefer?

27. Would you rather work in the morning or in the evening?

28. If you take a vacation, do you spend it in studying mathematics (if so, to what extent?) or do you devote the entire time to rest and relaxation?

Final remarks. *Of course, there may be many other details which it would be useful to learn by an inquiry: 29a. Does one work better standing, seated or lying down; b. at the blackboard or on paper; c. to what extent is one disturbed by outside noises; d. can one pursue a problem while walking or in a train; e. how do stimulants or sedatives (tobacco, coffee, alcohol, etc.) affect the quality and quantity of one's work?

*30. It would be very helpful for the purpose of psychological investigation to know what internal or mental images, what kind of "internal word" mathematicians make use of; whether they are motor, auditory, visual, or mixed, depending on the subject which they are studying.

If any persons who have been well acquainted with defunct mathematicians are able to furnish answers to any of the preceding questions, we ask them instantly to be kind enough to do so.

In this way they will make an important contribution to the history and development of mathematical science.

Added by the writer. The final question 30 corresponds to our discussion of Section VI, and it would be especially important to get further answers on it. Such answers ought to be of two different kinds, corresponding respectively to ordinary thought and to research effort.

Moreover, question 30 should be usefully supplemented by

31a. Especially in research thought, do the mental pictures or internal words present themselves in the full consciousness or in the fringe-consciousness (such as defined in Wallas's *Art of Thought*, pp. 51, 95 or under the name "antechamber of consciousness" in Galton's *Inquiries into Human Faculty*, p. 203 of the edition of 1883; p. 146 of the edition of 1910)?

31b. The same question is asked concerning the arguments which these mental pictures or words may symbolize.[3]

---

[3] Only a few mathematicians, until now, have answered questions 31a, and 31b, especially as concerns topological arguments such as the proof of Jordan's theorem (see Section VII, p. 103). For all of them without any exception, it is the geometrical aspect of the argument which directly appears in the full consciousness. One or two of them immediately feel the possibility of arithmetizing any link of it and are even able to find that arithmetization (so that it must be present in their fringe-consciousness); for others, it would require more or less effort.

APPENDIX II

A TESTIMONIAL FROM PROFESSOR EINSTEIN

Concerning the subject of the above study and, especially, matters treated in Section VI, the writer has received several answers to the questions which he has asked. All of them were valuable to him, but one is more important than any other, not only because of the personality of its author, but also as dealing with the question in a quite circumstantial and thorough manner. We owe it to the great scientist Albert Einstein, and it reads as follows:[1]

MY DEAR COLLEAGUE:

In the following, I am trying to answer in brief your questions as well as I am able. I am not satisfied myself with those answers and I am willing to answer more questions if you believe this could be of any advantage for the very interesting and difficult work you have undertaken.

(A) The words or the language, as they are written or spoken, do not seem to play any role in my mechanism of thought. The psychical entities which seem to serve as elements in thought are certain signs and more or less clear images which can be "voluntarily" reproduced and combined.

There is, of course, a certain connection between those elements and relevant logical concepts. It is also clear that the desire to arrive finally at logically connected concepts is the emotional basis of this rather vague play with the above mentioned elements. But taken from a psychological viewpoint, this combinatory play seems to be the essential feature in productive thought—before there is any connection with logical construction in words or other kinds of signs which can be communicated to others.

[1] Questions (A), (B), (C) correspond to number 30 of the questionnaire issued by *L'Enseignement Mathématique* (see Appendix I).

I have asked question (D) on the psychological type, not in research but in usual thought.

Question (E) corresponds to our number 31.

(B) The above mentioned elements are, in my case, of visual and some of muscular type. Conventional words or other signs have to be sought for laboriously only in a secondary stage, when the mentioned associative play is sufficiently established and can be reproduced at will.

(C) According to what has been said, the play with the mentioned elements is aimed to be analogous to certain logical connections one is searching for.

(D) Visual and motor. In a stage when words intervene at all, they are, in my case, purely auditive, but they interfere only in a secondary stage as already mentioned.

(E) It seems to me that what you call full consciousness is a limit case which can never be fully accomplished. This seems to me connected with the fact called the narrowness of consciousness (Enge des Bewusstseins).

Remark: Professor Max Wertheimer has tried to investigate the distinction between mere associating or combining of reproducible elements and between understanding (organisches Begreifen); I cannot judge how far his psychological analysis catches the essential point.[2]

With kind regards . . .

ALBERT EINSTEIN

[2] As can be seen, phenomena in Professor Einstein's mind are substantially analogous to those mentioned in Section VI, with, as natural, special features in several details. A more important and remarkable difference concerns question (E), i.e., the role of fringe- or full consciousness. Professor Einstein refers to the "narrowness of consciousness": a subject which we should have spoken of in our Section II if we had not been afraid of being carried too far afield, and a treatment of which will be found in William James's *Psychology*, Chap. XIII, pp. 217 ff.

It would be interesting to compare Max Wertheimer's ideas (connected with the Gestaltist school) not only with our Section VI, but with the first part of Section VII.

APPENDIX III

THE INVENTION OF INFINITESIMAL CALCULUS

In addition to the case of Pascal (p. 53), other similar occurrences have happened in the history of science. One of the most striking instances in modern times is the invention of Infinitesimal Calculus.

Heraclitus's profound idea that everything ought to be considered in its *"devenir,"* i.e. in its continuous transformation, had not been understood during Antiquity. Only in the fourteenth century A.D. did one of the greatest medieval thinkers, Nicole Oresme, notice that the rate of increase or decrease of a quantity is slowest in the neighborhood of a maximum or minimum. The bearing of such a remark was not perceived by anybody, including Oresme himself, to whom it did not appear that such a fundamental idea had to be developed.

Three centuries later the same principle was enunciated by Johannes Kepler, but Kepler went no further than Oresme had already gone before him; the discovery went only halfway.

Then, in Fermat's hands, the principle received mathematical expression. In several instances, considering one quantity in terms of another (such as time), Fermat used a mathematical operation which gave zero as the result if the quantity in question was a maximum or minimum. Moreover, the same method allowed him to find tangents to several curves considered by his contemporaries.

The operation performed by Fermat is precisely what we now call differentiation. Does this mean, as many are inclined to think, that he invented the Differential Calculus? In one sense we must answer "yes," for we see him applying his method to various problems, and even pointing out that the method could be applied to similar ones.[1] But in another sense we must say "no," for the method he used appeared to nobody in his time, not even to him-

[1] I am indebted for this information to the kindness of Professor Sergescu.

self, as a general rule for solving a whole class of problems, or as a new conception the properties of which deserved further investigation. Adapting an expression of Poincaré, we can say that things are more or less discovered, *not* discovered outright from complete obscurity to complete revelation. One step consists in acquiring the idea of a principle; another, if not several others, in giving a precise form to that idea and driving it far enough to be able to make it a starting point for further researches. In the present case, this was the work of Newton and Leibniz.

But the Differential Calculus is not the whole Infinitesimal Calculus. There is a second branch, the Integral Calculus, the fundamental operation of which is the valuation of plane curvilinear areas; and this implies a discovery which lay deep and had been entirely unsuspected, viz. the fact that integration is nothing else than the converse of differentiation. Who made that essential and difficult discovery? In the development of differentiation something of it was in the making. Torricelli and Fermat (perhaps even, though doubtful, Descartes) used methods which looked like the application of the principle and were indeed rather near it, but with a fundamental difference. I should say the same even of Barrow, Newton's master, in his *Lectiones Geometricae,* although the essential content of the n° 11 of his xth lecture is really equivalent to that principle.[2] Besides Descartes, who did not let the connection appear clearly, both Torricelli and Fermat treated special cases whose properties concealed the general principle; while for Barrow the true meaning of the principle was hidden by the meaning he gave to the notion of the tangent.

Thus Oresme, Kepler, and Fermat failed to discover the Differential Calculus because they did not pursue their initial and fruitful ideas.

We see how psychological considerations can be illustrated by the history of science; and conversely, how they can help us to understand correctly a question which, very often, can be considered as a badly set one: Who is the author of such or such a discovery?

[2] It is not certain whether Barrow was not influenced by his immortal disciple, whose genius he recognized.

CATALOG OF DOVER BOOKS

Books Explaining Science and Mathematics

WHAT IS SCIENCE?, N. Campbell. The role of experiment and measurement, the function of mathematics, the nature of scientific laws, the difference between laws and theories, the limitations of science, and many similarly provocative topics are treated clearly and without technicalities by an eminent scientist. "Still an excellent introduction to scientific philosophy," H. Margenau in PHYSICS TODAY. "A first-rate primer . . . deserves a wide audience," SCIENTIFIC AMERICAN. 192pp. 5⅜ x 8. S43 Paperbound **$1.25**

THE NATURE OF PHYSICAL THEORY, P. W. Bridgman. A Nobel Laureate's clear, non-technical lectures on difficulties and paradoxes connected with frontier research on the physical sciences. Concerned with such central concepts as thought, logic, mathematics, relativity, probability, wave mechanics, etc. he analyzes the contributions of such men as Newton, Einstein, Bohr, Heisenberg, and many others. "Lucid and entertaining . . . recommended to anyone who wants to get some insight into current philosophies of science," THE NEW PHILOSOPHY. Index. xi + 138pp. 5⅜ x 8. S33 Paperbound **$1.25**

EXPERIMENT AND THEORY IN PHYSICS, Max Born. A Nobel Laureate examines the nature of experiment and theory in theoretical physics and analyzes the advances made by the great physicists of our day: Heisenberg, Einstein, Bohr, Planck, Dirac, and others. The actual process of creation is detailed step-by-step by one who participated. A fine examination of the scientific method at work. 44pp. 5⅜ x 8. S308 Paperbound **75¢**

THE PSYCHOLOGY OF INVENTION IN THE MATHEMATICAL FIELD, J. Hadamard. The reports of such men as Descartes, Pascal, Einstein, Poincaré, and others are considered in this investigation of the method of idea-creation in mathematics and other sciences and the thinking process in general. How do ideas originate? What is the role of the unconscious? What is Poincaré's forgetting hypothesis? are some of the fascinating questions treated. A penetrating analysis of Einstein's thought processes concludes the book. xiii + 145pp. 5⅜ x 8. T107 Paperbound **$1.25**

THE NATURE OF LIGHT AND COLOUR IN THE OPEN AIR, M. Minnaert. Why are shadows sometimes blue, sometimes green, or other colors depending on the light and surroundings? What causes mirages? Why do multiple suns and moons appear in the sky? Professor Minnaert explains these unusual phenomena and hundreds of others in simple, easy-to-understand terms based on optical laws and the properties of light and color. No mathematics is required but artists, scientists, students, and everyone fascinated by these "tricks" of nature will find thousands of useful and amazing pieces of information. Hundreds of observational experiments are suggested which require no special equipment. 200 illustrations; 42 photos. xvi + 362pp. 5⅜ x 8. T196 Paperbound **$1.95**

THE UNIVERSE OF LIGHT, W. Bragg. Sir William Bragg, Nobel Laureate and great modern physicist, is also well known for his powers of clear exposition. Here he analyzes all aspects of light for the layman: lenses, reflection, refraction, the optics of vision, x-rays, the photoelectric effect, etc. He tells you what causes the color of spectra, rainbows, and soap bubbles, how magic mirrors work, and much more. Dozens of simple experiments are described. Preface. Index. 199 line drawings and photographs, including 2 full-page color plates. x + 283pp. 5⅜ x 8. T538 Paperbound **$1.85**

SOAP-BUBBLES: THEIR COLOURS AND THE FORCES THAT MOULD THEM, C. V. Boys. For continuing popularity and validity as scientific primer, few books can match this volume of easily-followed experiments, explanations. Lucid exposition of complexities of liquid films, surface tension and related phenomena, bubbles' reaction to heat, motion, music, magnetic fields. Experiments with capillary attraction, soap bubbles on frames, composite bubbles, liquid cylinders and jets, bubbles other than soap, etc. Wonderful introduction to scientific method, natural laws that have many ramifications in areas of modern physics. Only complete edition in print. New Introduction by S. Z. Lewin, New York University. 83 illustrations; 1 full-page color plate. xii + 190pp. 5⅜ x 8½. T542 Paperbound **95¢**

CATALOGUE OF DOVER BOOKS

THE STORY OF X-RAYS FROM RONTGEN TO ISOTOPES, A. R. Bleich, M.D. This book, by a member of the American College of Radiology, gives the scientific explanation of x-rays, their applications in medicine, industry and art, and their danger (and that of atmospheric radiation) to the individual and the species. You learn how radiation therapy is applied against cancer, how x-rays diagnose heart disease and other ailments, how they are used to examine mummies for information on diseases of early societies, and industrial materials for hidden weaknesses. 54 illustrations show x-rays of flowers, bones, stomach, gears with flaws, etc. 1st publication. Index. xix + 186pp. 5⅜ x 8.   T622 Paperbound **$1.35**

SPINNING TOPS AND GYROSCOPIC MOTION, John Perry. A classic elementary text of the dynamics of rotation — the behavior and use of rotating bodies such as gyroscopes and tops. In simple, everyday English you are shown how quasi-rigidity is induced in discs of paper, smoke rings, chains, etc., by rapid motions; why a gyrostat falls and why a top rises; precession; how the earth's motion affects climate; and many other phenomena. Appendix on practical use of gyroscopes. 62 figures. 128pp. 5⅜ x 8.   T416 Paperbound **$1.00**

SNOW CRYSTALS, W. A. Bentley, M. J. Humphreys. For almost 50 years W. A. Bentley photographed snow flakes in his laboratory in Jericho, Vermont; in 1931 the American Meteorological Society gathered together the best of his work, some 2400 photographs of snow flakes, plus a few ice flowers, windowpane frosts, dew, frozen rain, and other ice formations. Pictures were selected for beauty and scientific value. A very valuable work to anyone in meteorology, cryology; most interesting to layman; extremely useful for artist who wants beautiful, crystalline designs. All copyright free. Unabridged reprint of 1931 edition. 2453 illustrations. 227pp. 8 x 10½.   T287 Paperbound **$2.95**

A DOVER SCIENCE SAMPLER, edited by George Barkin. A collection of brief, non-technical passages from 44 Dover Books Explaining Science for the enjoyment of the science-minded browser. Includes work of Bertrand Russell, Poincaré, Laplace, Max Born, Galileo, Newton; material on physics, mathematics, metallurgy, anatomy, astronomy, chemistry, etc. You will be fascinated by Martin Gardner's analysis of the sincere pseudo-scientist, Moritz's account of Newton's absentmindedness, Bernard's examples of human vivisection, etc. Illustrations from the Diderot Pictorial Encyclopedia and De Re Metallica. 64 pages.   **FREE**

THE STORY OF ATOMIC THEORY AND ATOMIC ENERGY. J. G. Feinberg. A broader approach to subject of nuclear energy and its cultural implications than any other similar source. Very readable, informal, completely non-technical text. Begins with first atomic theory, 600 B.C. and carries you through the work of Mendelejeff, Röntgen, Madame Curie, to Einstein's equation and the A-bomb. New chapter goes through thermonuclear fission, binding energy, other events up to 1959. Radioactive decay and radiation hazards, future benefits, work of Bohr, moderns, hundreds more topics. "Deserves special mention . . . not only authoritative but thoroughly popular in the best sense of the word," Saturday Review. Formerly, "The Atom Story." Expanded with new chapter. Three appendixes. Index. 34 illustrations. vii + 243pp. 5⅜ x 8.   T625 Paperbound **$1.45**

THE STRANGE STORY OF THE QUANTUM, AN ACCOUNT FOR THE GENERAL READER OF THE GROWTH OF IDEAS UNDERLYING OUR PRESENT ATOMIC KNOWLEDGE, B. Hoffmann. Presents lucidly and expertly, with barest amount of mathematics, the problems and theories which led to modern quantum physics. Dr. Hoffmann begins with the closing years of the 19th century, when certain trifling discrepancies were noticed, and with illuminating analogies and examples takes you through the brilliant concepts of Planck, Einstein, Pauli, Broglie, Bohr, Schroedinger, Heisenberg, Dirac, Sommerfeld, Feynman, etc. This edition includes a new, long postscript carrying the story through 1958. "Of the books attempting an account of the history and contents of our modern atomic physics which have come to my attention, this is the best," H. Margenau, Yale University, in "American Journal of Physics." 32 tables and line illustrations. Index. 275pp. 5⅜ x 8.   T518 Paperbound **$1.45**

SPACE AND TIME, E. Borel. Written by a versatile mathematician of world renown with his customary lucidity and precision, this introduction to relativity for the layman presents scores of examples, analogies, and illustrations that open up new ways of thinking about space and time. It covers abstract geometry and geographical maps, continuity and topology, the propagation of light, the special theory of relativity, the general theory of relativity, theoretical researches, and much more. Mathematical notes. 2 Indexes. 4 Appendices. 15 figures. xvi + 243pp. 5⅜ x 8.   T592 Paperbound **$1.45**

FROM EUCLID TO EDDINGTON: A STUDY OF THE CONCEPTIONS OF THE EXTERNAL WORLD, Sir Edmund Whittaker. A foremost British scientist traces the development of theories of natural philosophy from the western rediscovery of Euclid to Eddington, Einstein, Dirac, etc. The inadequacy of classical physics is contrasted with present day attempts to understand the physical world through relativity, non-Euclidean geometry, space curvature, wave mechanics, etc. 5 major divisions of examination: Space; Time and Movement; the Concepts of Classical Physics; the Concepts of Quantum Mechanics; the Eddington Universe. 212pp. 5⅜ x 8.   T491 Paperbound **$1.35**

CATALOGUE OF DOVER BOOKS

Nature, Biology

NATURE RECREATION: Group Guidance for the Out-of-doors, William Gould Vinal. Intended for both the uninitiated nature instructor and the education student on the college level, this complete "how-to" program surveys the entire area of nature education for the young. Philosophy of nature recreation; requirements, responsibilities, important information for group leaders; nature games; suggested group projects; conducting meetings and getting discussions started; etc. Scores of immediately applicable teaching aids, plus completely updated sources of information, pamphlets, field guides, recordings, etc. Bibliography. 74 photographs. + 310pp. 5⅜ x 8½.   T1015 Paperbound **$1.75**

HOW TO KNOW THE WILD FLOWERS, Mrs. William Starr Dana. Classic nature book that has introduced thousands to wonders of American wild flowers. Color-season principle of organization is easy to use, even by those with no botanical training, and the genial, refreshing discussions of history, folklore, uses of over 1,000 native and escape flowers, foliage plants are informative as well as fun to read. Over 170 full-page plates, collected from several editions, may be colored in to make permanent records of finds. Revised to conform with 1950 edition of Gray's Manual of Botany. xlii + 438pp. 5⅜ x 8½.   T332 Paperbound **$1.85**

HOW TO KNOW THE FERNS, F. T. Parsons. Ferns, among our most lovely native plants, are all too little known. This classic of nature lore will enable the layman to identify almost any American fern he may come across. After an introduction on the structure and life of ferns, the 57 most important ferns are fully pictured and described (arranged upon a simple identification key). Index of Latin and English names. 61 illustrations and 42 full-page plates. xiv + 215pp. 5⅜ x 8.   T740 Paperbound **$1.25**

MANUAL OF THE TREES OF NORTH AMERICA, Charles Sprague Sargent. Still unsurpassed as most comprehensive, reliable study of North American tree characteristics, precise locations and distribution. By dean of American dendrologists. Every tree native to U.S., Canada, Alaska, 185 genera, 717 species, described in detail—leaves, flowers, fruit, winterbuds, bark, wood, growth habits etc. plus discussion of varieties and local variants, immaturity variations. Over 100 keys, including unusual 11-page analytical key to genera, aid in identification. 783 clear illustrations of flowers, fruit, leaves. An unmatched permanent reference work for all nature lovers. Second enlarged (1926) edition. Synopsis of families. Analytical key to genera. Glossary of technical terms. Index. 783 illustrations, 1 map. Two volumes. Total of 982pp. 5⅜ x 8.   T277 Vol. I Paperbound **$2.00**
                                                                               T278 Vol. II Paperbound **$2.00**
                                                                               The set **$4.00**

TREES OF THE EASTERN AND CENTRAL UNITED STATES AND CANADA, W. M. Harlow. A revised edition of a standard middle-level guide to native trees and important escapes. More than 140 trees are described in detail, and illustrated with more than 600 drawings and photographs. Supplementary keys will enable the careful reader to identify almost any tree he might encounter. xiii + 288pp. 5⅜ x 8.   T395 Paperbound **$1.35**

GUIDE TO SOUTHERN TREES, Ellwood S. Harrar and J. George Harrar. All the essential information about trees indigenous to the South, in an extremely handy format. Introductory essay on methods of tree classification and study, nomenclature, chief divisions of Southern trees, etc. Approximately 100 keys and synopses allow for swift, accurate identification of trees. Numerous excellent illustrations, non-technical text make this a useful book for teachers of biology or natural science, nature lovers, amateur naturalists. Revised 1962 edition. Index. Bibliography. Glossary of technical terms. 920 illustrations; 201 full-page plates. ix + 709pp. 4⅝ x 6⅜.   T945 Paperbound **$2.25**

FRUIT KEY AND TWIG KEY TO TREES AND SHRUBS, W. M. Harlow. Bound together in one volume for the first time, these handy and accurate keys to fruit and twig identification are the only guides of their sort with photographs (up to 3 times natural size). "Fruit Key": Key to over 120 different deciduous and evergreen fruits. 139 photographs and 11 line drawings. Synoptic summary of fruit types. Bibliography. 2 Indexes (common and scientific names). "Twig Key": Key to over 160 different twigs and buds. 173 photographs. Glossary of technical terms. Bibliography. 2 Indexes (common and scientific names). Two volumes bound as one. Total of xvii + 126pp. 5⅝ x 8⅜.   T511 Paperbound **$1.25**

INSECT LIFE AND INSECT NATURAL HISTORY, S. W. Frost. A work emphasizing habits, social life, and ecological relations of insects, rather than more academic aspects of classification and morphology. Prof. Frost's enthusiasm and knowledge are everywhere evident as he discusses insect associations and specialized habits like leaf-rolling, leaf-mining, and casemaking, the gall insects, the boring insects, aquatic insects, etc. He examines all sorts of matters not usually covered in general works, such as: insects as human food, insect music and musicians, insect response to electric and radio waves, use of insects in art and literature. The admirably executed purpose of this book, which covers the middle ground between elementary treatment and scholarly monographs, is to excite the reader to observe for himself. Over 700 illustrations. Extensive bibliography. x + 524pp. 5⅜ x 8.   T517 Paperbound **$2.45**

CATALOGUE OF DOVER BOOKS

COMMON SPIDERS OF THE UNITED STATES, J. H. Emerton. Here is a nature hobby you can pursue right in your own cellar! Only non-technical, but thorough, reliable guide to spiders for the layman. Over 200 spiders from all parts of the country, arranged by scientific classification, are identified by shape and color, number of eyes, habitat and range, habits, etc. Full text, 501 line drawings and photographs, and valuable introduction explain webs, poisons, threads, capturing and preserving spiders, etc. Index. New synoptic key by S. W. Frost. xxiv + 225pp. 5⅜ x 8. T223 Paperbound **$1.35**

THE LIFE STORY OF THE FISH: HIS MANNERS AND MORALS, Brian Curtis. A comprehensive, non-technical survey of just about everything worth knowing about fish. Written for the aquarist, the angler, and the layman with an inquisitive mind, the text covers such topics as evolution, external covering and protective coloration, physics and physiology of vision, maintenance of equilibrium, function of the lateral line canal for auditory and temperature senses, nervous system, function of the air bladder, reproductive system and methods—courtship, mating, spawning, care of young—and many more. Also sections on game fish, the problems of conservation and a fascinating chapter on fish curiosities. "Clear, simple language . . . excellent judgment in choice of subjects . . . delightful sense of humor," New York Times. Revised (1949) edition. Index. Bibliography of 72 items. 6 full-page photographic plates. xii + 284pp. 5⅜ x 8. T929 Paperbound **$1.50**

BATS, Glover Morrill Allen. The most comprehensive study of bats as a life-form by the world's foremost authority. A thorough summary of just about everything known about this fascinating and mysterious flying mammal, including its unique location sense, hibernation and cycles, its habitats and distribution, its wing structure and flying habits, and its relationship to man in the long history of folklore and superstition. Written on a middle-level, the book can be profitably studied by a trained zoologist and thoroughly enjoyed by the layman. "An absorbing text with excellent illustrations. Bats should have more friends and fewer thoughtless detractors as a result of the publication of this volume," William Beebe, Books. Extensive bibliography. 57 photographs and illustrations. x + 368pp. 5⅜ x 8½. T984 Paperbound **$2.00**

BIRDS AND THEIR ATTRIBUTES, Glover Morrill Allen. A fine general introduction to birds as living organisms, especially valuable because of emphasis on structure, physiology, habits, behavior. Discusses relationship of bird to man, early attempts at scientific ornithology, feathers and coloration, skeletal structure including bills, legs and feet, wings. Also food habits, evolution and present distribution, feeding and nest-building, still unsolved questions of migrations and location sense, many more similar topics. Final chapter on classification, nomenclature. A good popular-level summary for the biologist; a first-rate introduction for the layman. Reprint of 1925 edition. References and index. 51 illustrations. viii + 338pp. 5⅜ x 8½. T957 Paperbound **$1.85**

LIFE HISTORIES OF NORTH AMERICAN BIRDS, Arthur Cleveland Bent. Bent's monumental series of books on North American birds, prepared and published under auspices of Smithsonian Institute, is the definitive coverage of the subject, the most-used single source of information. Now the entire set is to be made available by Dover in inexpensive editions. This encyclopedic collection of detailed, specific observations utilizes reports of hundreds of contemporary observers, writings of such naturalists as Audubon, Burroughs, William Brewster, as well as author's own extensive investigations. Contains literally everything known about life history of each bird considered: nesting, eggs, plumage, distribution and migration, voice, enemies, courtship, etc. These not over-technical works are musts for ornithologists, conservationists, amateur naturalists, anyone seriously interested in American birds.

BIRDS OF PREY. More than 100 subspecies of hawks, falcons, eagles, buzzards, condors and owls, from the common barn owl to the extinct caracara of Guadaloupe Island. 400 photographs. Two volume set. Index for each volume. Bibliographies of 403, 520 items. 197 full-page plates. Total of 907pp. 5⅜ x 8½.
Vol. I T931 Paperbound **$2.35**
Vol. II T932 Paperbound **$2.35**

WILD FOWL. Ducks, geese, swans, and tree ducks—73 different subspecies. Two volume set. Index for each volume. Bibliographies of 124, 144 items. 106 full-page plates. Total of 685pp. 5⅜ x 8½.
Vol. I T285 Paperbound **$2.35**
Vol. II T286 Paperbound **$2.35**

SHORE BIRDS. 81 varieties (sandpipers, woodcocks, plovers, snipes, phalaropes, curlews, oyster catchers, etc.). More than 200 photographs of eggs, nesting sites, adult and young of important species. Two volume set. Index for each volume. Bibliographies of 261, 188 items. 121 full-page plates. Total of 860pp. 5⅜ x 8½.
Vol. I T933 Paperbound **$2.35**
Vol. II T934 Paperbound **$2.35**

THE LIFE OF PASTEUR, R. Vallery-Radot. 13th edition of this definitive biography, cited in Encyclopaedia Britannica. Authoritative, scholarly, well-documented with contemporary quotes, observations; gives complete picture of Pasteur's personal life; especially thorough presentation of scientific activities with silkworms, fermentation, hydrophobia, inoculation, etc. Introduction by Sir William Osler. Index. 505pp. 5⅜ x 8. T632 Paperbound **$2.00**

Puzzles, Mathematical Recreations

SYMBOLIC LOGIC and THE GAME OF LOGIC, Lewis Carroll. "Symbolic Logic" is not concerned with modern symbolic logic, but is instead a collection of over 380 problems posed with charm and imagination, using the syllogism, and a fascinating diagrammatic method of drawing conclusions. In "The Game of Logic" Carroll's whimsical imagination devises a logical game played with 2 diagrams and counters (included) to manipulate hundreds of tricky syllogisms. The final section, "Hit or Miss" is a lagniappe of 101 additional puzzles in the delightful Carroll manner. Until this reprint edition, both of these books were rarities costing up to $15 each. Symbolic Logic: Index. xxxi + 199pp. The Game of Logic: 96pp. 2 vols. bound as one. 5⅜ x 8.   T492 Paperbound **$1.50**

PILLOW PROBLEMS and A TANGLED TALE, Lewis Carroll. One of the rarest of all Carroll's works, "Pillow Problems" contains 72 original math puzzles, all typically ingenious. Particularly fascinating are Carroll's answers which remain exactly as he thought them out, reflecting his actual mental process. The problems in "A Tangled Tale" are in story form, originally appearing as a monthly magazine serial. Carroll not only gives the solutions, but uses answers sent in by readers to discuss wrong approaches and misleading paths, and grades them for insight. Both of these books were rarities until this edition, "Pillow Problems" costing up to $25, and "A Tangled Tale" $15. Pillow Problems: Preface and Introduction by Lewis Carroll. xx + 109pp. A Tangled Tale: 6 illustrations. 152pp. Two vols. bound as one. 5⅜ x 8.   T493 Paperbound **$1.50**

AMUSEMENTS IN MATHEMATICS, Henry Ernest Dudeney. The foremost British originator of mathematical puzzles is always intriguing, witty, and paradoxical in this classic, one of the largest collections of mathematical amusements. More than 430 puzzles, problems, and paradoxes. Mazes and games, problems on number manipulation, unicursal and other route problems, puzzles on measuring, weighing, packing, age, kinship, chessboards, joiners', crossing river, plane figure dissection, and many others. Solutions. More than 450 illustrations. vii + 258pp. 5⅜ x 8.   T473 Paperbound **$1.25**

THE CANTERBURY PUZZLES, Henry Dudeney. Chaucer's pilgrims set one another problems in story form. Also Adventures of the Puzzle Club, the Strange Escape of the King's Jester, the Monks of Riddlewell, the Squire's Christmas Puzzle Party, and others. All puzzles are original, based on dissecting plane figures, arithmetic, algebra, elementary calculus and other branches of mathematics, and purely logical ingenuity. "The limit of ingenuity and intricacy," The Observer. Over 110 puzzles. Full Solutions. 150 illustrations. vii + 225pp. 5⅜ x 8.
T474 Paperbound **$1.25**

MATHEMATICAL EXCURSIONS, H. A. Merrill. Even if you hardly remember your high school math, you'll enjoy the 90 stimulating problems contained in this book and you will come to understand a great many mathematical principles with surprisingly little effort. Many useful shortcuts and diversions not generally known are included: division by inspection, Russian peasant multiplication, memory systems for pi, building odd and even magic squares, square roots by geometry, dyadic systems, and many more. Solutions to difficult problems. 50 illustrations. 145pp. 5⅜ x 8.   T350 Paperbound **$1.00**

MAGIC SQUARES AND CUBES, W. S. Andrews. Only book-length treatment in English, a thorough non-technical description and analysis. Here are nasik, overlapping, pandiagonal, serrated squares; magic circles, cubes, spheres, rhombuses. Try your hand at 4-dimensional magical figures! Much unusual folklore and tradition included. High school algebra is sufficient. 754 diagrams and illustrations. viii + 419pp. 5⅜ x 8.   T658 Paperbound **$1.85**

CALIBAN'S PROBLEM BOOK: MATHEMATICAL, INFERENTIAL AND CRYPTOGRAPHIC PUZZLES, H. Phillips (Caliban), S. T. Shovelton, G. S. Marshall. 105 ingenious problems by the greatest living creator of puzzles based on logic and inference. Rigorous, modern, piquant; reflecting their author's unusual personality, these intermediate and advanced puzzles all involve the ability to reason clearly through complex situations; some call for mathematical knowledge, ranging from algebra to number theory. Solutions. xi + 180pp. 5⅜ x 8.
T736 Paperbound **$1.25**

MATHEMATICAL PUZZLES FOR BEGINNERS AND ENTHUSIASTS, G. Mott-Smith. 188 mathematical puzzles based on algebra, dissection of plane figures, permutations, and probability, that will test and improve your powers of inference and interpretation. The Odic Force, The Spider's Cousin, Ellipse Drawing, theory and strategy of card and board games like tit-tat-toe, go moku, salvo, and many others. 100 pages of detailed mathematical explanations. Appendix of primes, square roots, etc. 135 illustrations. 2nd revised edition. 248pp. 5⅜ x 8.
T198 Paperbound **$1.00**

MATHEMAGIC, MAGIC PUZZLES, AND GAMES WITH NUMBERS, R. V. Heath. More than 60 new puzzles and stunts based on the properties of numbers. Easy techniques for multiplying large numbers mentally, revealing hidden numbers magically, finding the date of any day in any year, and dozens more. Over 30 pages devoted to magic squares, triangles, cubes, circles, etc. Edited by J. S. Meyer. 76 illustrations. 128pp. 5⅜ x 8.   T110 Paperbound **$1.00**

CATALOGUE OF DOVER BOOKS

THE BOOK OF MODERN PUZZLES, G. L. Kaufman. A completely new series of puzzles as fascinating as crossword and deduction puzzles but based upon different principles and techniques. Simple 2-minute teasers, word labyrinths, design and pattern puzzles, logic and observation puzzles — over 150 braincrackers. Answers to all problems. 116 illustrations. 192pp. 5⅜ x 8.
T143 Paperbound **$1.00**

NEW WORD PUZZLES, G. L. Kaufman. 100 ENTIRELY NEW puzzles based on words and their combinations that will delight crossword puzzle, Scrabble and Jotto fans. Chess words, based on the moves of the chess king; design-onyms, symmetrical designs made of synonyms; rhymed double-crostics; syllable sentences; addle letter anagrams; alphagrams; linkograms; and many others all brand new. Full solutions. Space to work problems. 196 figures. vi + 122pp. 5⅜ x 8.
T344 Paperbound **$1.00**

MAZES AND LABYRINTHS: A BOOK OF PUZZLES, W. Shepherd. Mazes, formerly associated with mystery and ritual, are still among the most intriguing of intellectual puzzles. This is a novel and different collection of 50 amusements that embody the principle of the maze: mazes in the classical tradition; 3-dimensional, ribbon, and Möbius-strip mazes; hidden messages; spatial arrangements; etc.—almost all built on amusing story situations. 84 illustrations. Essay on maze psychology. Solutions. xv + 122pp. 5⅜ x 8.
T731 Paperbound **$1.00**

MAGIC TRICKS & CARD TRICKS, W. Jonson. Two books bound as one. 52 tricks with cards, 37 tricks with coins, bills, eggs, smoke, ribbons, slates, etc. Details on presentation, misdirection, and routining will help you master such famous tricks as the Changing Card, Card in the Pocket, Four Aces, Coin Through the Hand, Bill in the Egg, Afghan Bands, and over 75 others. If you follow the lucid exposition and key diagrams carefully, you will finish these two books with an astonishing mastery of magic. 106 figures. 224pp. 5⅜ x 8. T909 Paperbound **$1.00**

PANORAMA OF MAGIC, Milbourne Christopher. A profusely illustrated history of stage magic, a unique selection of prints and engravings from the author's private collection of magic memorabilia, the largest of its kind. Apparatus, stage settings and costumes; ingenious ads distributed by the performers and satiric broadsides passed around in the streets ridiculing pompous showmen; programs; decorative souvenirs. The lively text, by one of America's foremost professional magicians, is full of anecdotes about almost legendary wizards: Dede, the Egyptian; Philadelphia, the wonder-worker; Robert-Houdin, "the father of modern magic;" Harry Houdini; scores more. Altogether a pleasure package for anyone interested in magic, stage setting and design, ethnology, psychology, or simply in unusual people. A Dover original. 295 illustrations; 8 in full color. Index. viii + 216pp. 8⅜ x 11¼.
T774 Paperbound **$2.25**

HOUDINI ON MAGIC, Harry Houdini. One of the greatest magicians of modern times explains his most prized secrets. How locks are picked, with illustrated picks and skeleton keys; how a girl is sawed into twins; how to walk through a brick wall — Houdini's explanations of 44 stage tricks with many diagrams. Also included is a fascinating discussion of great magicians of the past and the story of his fight against fraudulent mediums and spiritualists. Edited by W.B. Gibson and M.N. Young. Bibliography. 155 figures, photos. xv + 280pp. 5⅜ x 8.
T384 Paperbound **$1.25**

MATHEMATICS, MAGIC AND MYSTERY, Martin Gardner. Why do card tricks work? How do magicians perform astonishing mathematical feats? How is stage mind-reading possible? This is the first book length study explaining the application of probability, set theory, theory of numbers, topology, etc., to achieve many startling tricks. Non-technical, accurate, detailed! 115 sections discuss tricks with cards, dice, coins, knots, geometrical vanishing illusions, how a Curry square "demonstrates" that the sum of the parts may be greater than the whole, and dozens of others. No sleight of hand necessary! 135 illustrations. xii + 174pp. 5⅜ x 8.
T335 Paperbound **$1.00**

EASY-TO-DO ENTERTAINMENTS AND DIVERSIONS WITH COINS, CARDS, STRING, PAPER AND MATCHES, R. M. Abraham. Over 300 tricks, games and puzzles will provide young readers with absorbing fun. Sections on card games; paper-folding; tricks with coins, matches and pieces of string; games for the agile; toy-making from common household objects; mathematical recreations; and 50 miscellaneous pastimes. Anyone in charge of groups of youngsters, including hard-pressed parents, and in need of suggestions on how to keep children sensibly amused and quietly content will find this book indispensable. Clear, simple text, copious number of delightful line drawings and illustrative diagrams. Originally titled "Winter Nights Entertainments." Introduction by Lord Baden Powell. 329 illustrations. v + 186pp. 5⅜ x 8½.
T921 Paperbound **$1.00**

STRING FIGURES AND HOW TO MAKE THEM, Caroline Furness Jayne. 107 string figures plus variations selected from the best primitive and modern examples developed by Navajo, Apache, pygmies of Africa, Eskimo, in Europe, Australia, China, etc. The most readily understandable, easy-to-follow book in English on perennially popular recreation. Crystal-clear exposition; step-by-step diagrams. Everyone from kindergarten children to adults looking for unusual diversion will be endlessly amused. Index. Bibliography. Introduction by A. C. Haddon. 17 full-page plates. 960 illustrations. xxiii + 401pp. 5⅜ x 8½.
T152 Paperbound **$2.00**

Entertainments, Humor

ODDITIES AND CURIOSITIES OF WORDS AND LITERATURE, C. Bombaugh, edited by M. Gardner. The largest collection of idiosyncratic prose and poetry techniques in English, a legendary work in the curious and amusing bypaths of literary recreations and the play technique in literature—so important in modern works. Contains alphabetic poetry, acrostics, palindromes, scissors verse, centos, emblematic poetry, famous literary puns, hoaxes, notorious slips of the press, hilarious mistranslations, and much more. Revised and enlarged with modern material by Martin Gardner. 368pp. 5⅜ x 8. T759 Paperbound **$1.50**

A NONSENSE ANTHOLOGY, collected by Carolyn Wells. 245 of the best nonsense verses ever written, including nonsense puns, absurd arguments, mock epics and sagas, nonsense ballads, odes, "sick" verses, dog-Latin verses, French nonsense verses, songs. By Edward Lear, Lewis Carroll, Gelett Burgess, W. S. Gilbert, Hilaire Belloc, Peter Newell, Oliver Herford, etc., 83 writers in all plus over four score anonymous nonsense verses. A special section of limericks, plus famous nonsense such as Carroll's "Jabberwocky" and Lear's "The Jumblies" and much excellent verse virtually impossible to locate elsewhere. For 50 years considered the best anthology available. Index of first lines specially prepared for this edition. Introduction by Carolyn Wells. 3 indexes: Title, Author, First lines. xxxiii + 279pp. T499 Paperbound **$1.25**

THE BAD CHILD'S BOOK OF BEASTS, MORE BEASTS FOR WORSE CHILDREN, and A MORAL ALPHABET, H. Belloc. Hardly an anthology of humorous verse has appeared in the last 50 years without at least a couple of these famous nonsense verses. But one must see the entire volumes—with all the delightful original illustrations by Sir Basil Blackwood—to appreciate fully Belloc's charming and witty verses that play so subacidly on the platitudes of life and morals that beset his day—and ours. A great humor classic. Three books in one. Total of 157pp. 5⅜ x 8. T749 Paperbound **$1.00**

THE DEVIL'S DICTIONARY, Ambrose Bierce. Sardonic and irreverent barbs puncturing the pomposities and absurdities of American politics, business, religion, literature, and arts, by the country's greatest satirist in the classic tradition. Epigrammatic as Shaw, piercing as Swift, American as Mark Twain, Will Rogers, and Fred Allen, Bierce will always remain the favorite of a small coterie of enthusiasts, and of writers and speakers whom he supplies with "some of the most gorgeous witticisms of the English language" (H. L. Mencken). Over 1000 entries in alphabetical order. 144pp. 5⅜ x 8. T487 Paperbound **$1.00**

THE PURPLE COW AND OTHER NONSENSE, Gelett Burgess. The best of Burgess's early nonsense, selected from the first edition of the "Burgess Nonsense Book." Contains many of his most unusual and truly awe-inspiring pieces: 36 nonsense quatrains, the Poems of Patagonia, Alphabet of Famous Goops, and the other hilarious (and rare) adult nonsense that place him in the forefront of American humorists. All pieces are accompanied by the original Burgess illustrations. 123 illustrations. xiii + 113pp. 5⅜ x 8. T772 Paperbound **$1.00**

MY PIOUS FRIENDS AND DRUNKEN COMPANIONS and MORE PIOUS FRIENDS AND DRUNKEN COMPANIONS, Frank Shay. Folksingers, amateur and professional, and everyone who loves singing: here, available for the first time in 30 years, is this valued collection of 132 ballads, blues, vaudeville numbers, drinking songs, sea chanties, comedy songs. Songs of pre-Beatnik Bohemia; songs from all over America, England, France, Australia; the great songs of the Naughty Nineties and early twentieth-century America. Over a third with music. Woodcuts by John Held, Jr. convey perfectly the brash insouciance of an era of rollicking unabashed song. 12 illustrations by John Held, Jr. Two indexes (Titles and First lines and Choruses). Introductions by the author. Two volumes bound as one. Total of xvi + 235pp. 5⅜ x 8½. T946 Paperbound **$1.00**

HOW TO TELL THE BIRDS FROM THE FLOWERS, R. W. Wood. How not to confuse a carrot with a parrot, a grape with an ape, a puffin with nuffin. Delightful drawings, clever puns, absurd little poems point out far-fetched resemblances in nature. The author was a leading physicist. Introduction by Margaret Wood White. 106 illus. 60pp. 5⅜ x 8. T523 Paperbound **75¢**

PECK'S BAD BOY AND HIS PA, George W. Peck. The complete edition, containing both volumes, of one of the most widely read American humor books. The endless ingenious pranks played by bad boy "Hennery" on his pa and the grocery man, the outraged pomposity of Pa, the perpetual ridiculing of middle class institutions, are as entertaining today as they were in 1883. No pale sophistications or subtleties, but rather humor vigorous, raw, earthy, imaginative, and, as folk humor often is, sadistic. This peculiarly fascinating book is also valuable to historians and students of American culture as a portrait of an age. 100 original illustrations by True Williams. Introduction by E. F. Bleiler. 347pp. 5⅜ x 8. T497 Paperbound **$1.35**

CATALOGUE OF DOVER BOOKS

THE HUMOROUS VERSE OF LEWIS CARROLL. Almost every poem Carroll ever wrote, the largest collection ever published, including much never published elsewhere: 150 parodies, burlesques, riddles, ballads, acrostics, etc., with 130 original illustrations by Tenniel, Carroll, and others. "Addicts will be grateful . . . there is nothing for the faithful to do but sit down and fall to the banquet," N. Y. Times. Index to first lines. xiv + 446pp. 5⅜ x 8.
T654 Paperbound **$1.85**

DIVERSIONS AND DIGRESSIONS OF LEWIS CARROLL. A major new treasure for Carroll fans! Rare privately published humor, fantasy, puzzles, and games by Carroll at his whimsical best, with a new vein of frank satire. Includes many new mathematical amusements and recreations, among them the fragmentary Part III of "Curiosa Mathematica." Contains "The Rectory Umbrella," "The New Belfry," "The Vision of the Three T's," and much more. New 32-page supplement of rare photographs taken by Carroll. x + 375pp. 5⅜ x 8.
T732 Paperbound **$1.65**

THE COMPLETE NONSENSE OF EDWARD LEAR. This is the only complete edition of this master of gentle madness available at a popular price. A BOOK OF NONSENSE, NONSENSE SONGS, MORE NONSENSE SONGS AND STORIES in their entirety with all the old favorites that have delighted children and adults for years. The Dong With A Luminous Nose, The Jumblies, The Owl and the Pussycat, and hundreds of other bits of wonderful nonsense. 214 limericks, 3 sets of Nonsense Botany, 5 Nonsense Alphabets, 546 drawings by Lear himself, and much more. 320pp. 5⅜ x 8.
T167 Paperbound **$1.00**

THE MELANCHOLY LUTE, The Humorous Verse of Franklin P. Adams ("FPA"). The author's own selection of light verse, drawn from thirty years of FPA's column, "The Conning Tower," syndicated all over the English-speaking world. Witty, perceptive, literate, these ninety-six poems range from parodies of other poets, Millay, Longfellow, Edgar Guest, Kipling, Masefield, etc., and free and hilarious translations of Horace and other Latin poets, to satiric comments on fabled American institutions—the New York Subways, preposterous ads, suburbanites, sensational journalism, etc. They reveal with vigor and clarity the humor, integrity and restraint of a wise and gentle American satirist. Introduction by Robert Hutchinson. vi + 122pp. 5⅜ x 8½.
T108 Paperbound **$1.00**

SINGULAR TRAVELS, CAMPAIGNS, AND ADVENTURES OF BARON MUNCHAUSEN, R. E. Raspe, with 90 illustrations by Gustave Doré. The first edition in over 150 years to reestablish the deeds of the Prince of Liars exactly as Raspe first recorded them in 1785—the genuine Baron Munchausen, one of the most popular personalities in English literature. Included also are the best of the many sequels, written by other hands. Introduction on Raspe by J. Carswell. Bibliography of early editions. xliv + 192pp. 5⅜ x 8.
T698 Paperbound **$1.00**

THE WIT AND HUMOR OF OSCAR WILDE, ed. by Alvin Redman. Wilde at his most brilliant, in 1000 epigrams exposing weaknesses and hypocrisies of "civilized" society. Divided into 49 categories—sin, wealth, women, America, etc.—to aid writers, speakers. Includes excerpts from his trials, books, plays, criticism. Formerly "The Epigrams of Oscar Wilde." Introduction by Vyvyan Holland, Wilde's only living son. Introductory essay by editor. 260pp. 5⅜ x 8.
T602 Paperbound **$1.00**

MAX AND MORITZ, Wilhelm Busch. Busch is one of the great humorists of all time, as well as the father of the modern comic strip. This volume, translated by H. A. Klein and other hands, contains the perennial favorite "Max and Moritz" (translated by C. T. Brooks), Plisch and Plum, Das Rabennest, Eispeter, and seven other whimsical, sardonic, jovial, diabolical cartoon and verse stories. Lively English translations parallel the original German. This work has delighted millions, since it first appeared in the 19th century, and is guaranteed to please almost anyone. Edited by H. A. Klein, with an afterword. x + 205pp. 5⅝ x 8½.
T181 Paperbound **$1.00**

HYPOCRITICAL HELENA, Wilhelm Busch. A companion volume to "Max and Moritz," with the title piece (Die Fromme Helena) and 10 other highly amusing cartoon and verse stories, all newly translated by H. A. Klein and M. C. Klein: Adventure on New Year's Eve (Abenteuer in der Neujahrsnacht), Hangover on the Morning after New Year's Eve (Der Katzenjammer am Neujahrsmorgen), etc. English and German in parallel columns. Hours of pleasure, also a fine language aid. x + 205pp. 5⅝ x 8½.
T184 Paperbound **$1.00**

THE BEAR THAT WASN'T, Frank Tashlin. What does it mean? Is it simply delightful wry humor, or a charming story of a bear who wakes up in the midst of a factory, or a satire on Big Business, or an existential cartoon-story of the human condition, or a symbolization of the struggle between conformity and the individual? New York Herald Tribune said of the first edition: ". . . a fable for grownups that will be fun for children. Sit down with the book and get your own bearings." Long an underground favorite with readers of all ages and opinions. v + 51pp. Illustrated. 5⅜ x 8½.
T939 Paperbound **75¢**

RUTHLESS RHYMES FOR HEARTLESS HOMES and MORE RUTHLESS RHYMES FOR HEARTLESS HOMES, Harry Graham ("Col. D. Streamer"). Two volumes of Little Willy and 48 other poetic disasters. A bright, new reprint of oft-quoted, never forgotten, devastating humor by a precursor of today's "sick" joke school. For connoisseurs of wicked, wacky humor and all who delight in the comedy of manners. Original drawings are a perfect complement. 61 illustrations. Index. vi + 69pp. Two vols. bound as one. 5⅜ x 8½.
T930 Paperbound **75¢**

CATALOGUE OF DOVER BOOKS

Say It language phrase books

These handy phrase books (128 to 196 pages each) make grammatical drills unnecessary for an elementary knowledge of a spoken foreign language. Covering most matters of travel and everyday life each volume contains:

Over 1000 phrases and sentences in immediately useful forms — foreign language plus English.

Modern usage designed for Americans. Specific phrases like, "Give me small change," and "Please call a taxi."

Simplified phonetic transcription you will be able to read at sight.

The only completely indexed phrase books on the market.

Covers scores of important situations: — Greetings, restaurants, sightseeing, useful expressions, etc.

These books are prepared by native linguists who are professors at Columbia, N.Y.U., Fordham and other great universities. Use them independently or with any other book or record course. They provide a supplementary living element that most other courses lack. Individual volumes in:

Russian 75¢	Italian 75¢	Spanish 75¢	German 75¢
Hebrew 75¢	Danish 75¢	Japanese 75¢	Swedish 75¢
Dutch 75¢	Esperanto 75¢	Modern Greek 75¢	Portuguese 75¢
Norwegian 75¢	Polish 75¢	French 75¢	Yiddish 75¢
Turkish 75¢		English for German-speaking people 75¢	
English for Italian-speaking people 75¢		English for Spanish-speaking people 75¢	

Large clear type. 128-196 pages each. 3½ x 5¼. Sturdy paper binding.

Listen and Learn language records

LISTEN & LEARN is the only language record course designed especially to meet your travel and everyday needs. It is available in separate sets for FRENCH, SPANISH, GERMAN, JAPANESE, RUSSIAN, MODERN GREEK, PORTUGUESE, ITALIAN and HEBREW, and each set contains three 33⅓ rpm long-playing records—1½ hours of recorded speech by eminent native speakers who are professors at Columbia, New York University, Queens College.

Check the following special features found only in LISTEN & LEARN:

- **Dual-language recording. 812 selected phrases and sentences**, over 3200 words, spoken first in English, then in their foreign language equivalents. A suitable pause follows each foreign phrase, allowing you time to repeat the expression. You learn by unconscious assimilation.

- **128 to 206-page manual** contains everything on the records, plus a simple phonetic pronunciation guide.

- **Indexed for convenience. The only set on the market** that is completely indexed. No more puzzling over where to find the phrase you need. Just look in the rear of the manual.

- **Practical.** No time wasted on material you can find in any grammar. LISTEN & LEARN covers central core material with phrase approach. Ideal for the person with limited learning time.

- **Living, modern expressions**, not found in other courses. Hygienic products, modern equipment, shopping—expressions used every day, like "nylon" and "air-conditioned."

- **Limited objective.** Everything you learn, no matter where you stop, is immediately useful. You have to finish other courses, wade through grammar and vocabulary drill, before they help you.

- **High-fidelity recording.** LISTEN & LEARN records equal in clarity and surface-silence any record on the market costing up to $6.

"Excellent . . . the spoken records . . . impress me as being among the very best on the market," **Prof. Mario Pei**, Dept. of Romance Languages, Columbia University. "Inexpensive and well-done . . . it would make an ideal present," CHICAGO SUNDAY TRIBUNE. "More genuinely helpful than anything of its kind which I have previously encountered," **Sidney Clark**, well-known author of "ALL THE BEST" travel books.

UNCONDITIONAL GUARANTEE. Try LISTEN & LEARN, then return it within 10 days for full refund if you are not satisfied.

Each set contains three twelve-inch 33⅓ records, manual, and album.

SPANISH	the set $5.95	GERMAN	the set $5.95
FRENCH	the set $5.95	ITALIAN	the set $5.95
RUSSIAN	the set $5.95	JAPANESE	the set $5.95
PORTUGUESE	the set $5.95	MODERN GREEK	the set $5.95
MODERN HEBREW	the set $5.95		

Americana

THE EYES OF DISCOVERY, J. Bakeless. A vivid reconstruction of how unspoiled America appeared to the first white men. Authentic and enlightening accounts of Hudson's landing in New York, Coronado's trek through the Southwest; scores of explorers, settlers, trappers, soldiers. America's pristine flora, fauna, and Indians in every region and state in fresh and unusual new aspects. "A fascinating view of what the land was like before the first highway went through," Time. 68 contemporary illustrations, 39 newly added in this edition. Index. Bibliography. x + 500pp. 5⅜ x 8. **T761 Paperbound $2.00**

AUDUBON AND HIS JOURNALS, J. J. Audubon. A collection of fascinating accounts of Europe and America in the early 1800's through Audubon's own eyes. Includes the Missouri River Journals —an eventful trip through America's untouched heartland, the Labrador Journals, the European Journals, the famous "Episodes", and other rare Audubon material, including the descriptive chapters from the original letterpress edition of the "Ornithological Studies", omitted in all later editions. Indispensable for ornithologists, naturalists, and all lovers of Americana and adventure. 70-page biography by Audubon's granddaughter. 38 illustrations. Index. Total of 1106pp. 5⅜ x 8.

T675 Vol I Paperbound $2.00
T676 Vol II Paperbound $2.00
The set $4.00

TRAVELS OF WILLIAM BARTRAM, edited by Mark Van Doren. The first inexpensive illustrated edition of one of the 18th century's most delightful books is an excellent source of first-hand material on American geography, anthropology, and natural history. Many descriptions of early Indian tribes are our only source of information on them prior to the infiltration of the white man. "The mind of a scientist with the soul of a poet," John Livingston Lowes. 13 original illustrations and maps. Edited with an introduction by Mark Van Doren. 448pp. 5⅜ x 8. **T13 Paperbound $2.00**

GARRETS AND PRETENDERS: A HISTORY OF BOHEMIANISM IN AMERICA, A. Parry. The colorful and fantastic history of American Bohemianism from Poe to Kerouac. This is the only complete record of hoboes, cranks, starving poets, and suicides. Here are Pfaff, Whitman, Crane, Bierce, Pound, and many others. New chapters by the author and by H. T. Moore bring this thorough and well-documented history down to the Beatniks. "An excellent account," N. Y. Times. Scores of cartoons, drawings, and caricatures. Bibliography. Index. xxviii + 421pp. 5⅝ x 8⅜. **T708 Paperbound $1.95**

THE EXPLORATION OF THE COLORADO RIVER AND ITS CANYONS, J. W. Powell. The thrilling first-hand account of the expedition that filled in the last white space on the map of the United States. Rapids, famine, hostile Indians, and mutiny are among the perils encountered as the unknown Colorado Valley reveals its secrets. This is the only uncut version of Major Powell's classic of exploration that has been printed in the last 60 years. Includes later reflections and subsequent expedition. 250 illustrations, new map. 400pp. 5⅝ x 8⅜. **T94 Paperbound $2.00**

THE JOURNAL OF HENRY D. THOREAU, Edited by Bradford Torrey and Francis H. Allen. Henry Thoreau is not only one of the most important figures in American literature and social thought; his voluminous journals (from which his books emerged as selections and crystallizations) constitute both the longest, most sensitive record of personal internal development and a most penetrating description of a historical moment in American culture. This present set, which was first issued in fourteen volumes, contains Thoreau's entire journals from 1837 to 1862, with the exception of the lost years which were found only recently. We are reissuing it, complete and unabridged, with a new introduction by Walter Harding, Secretary of the Thoreau Society. Fourteen volumes reissued in two volumes. Foreword by Henry Seidel Canby. Total of 1888pp. 8⅜ x 12¼. **T312-3 Two volume set, Clothbound $20.00**

GAMES AND SONGS OF AMERICAN CHILDREN, collected by William Wells Newell. A remarkable collection of 190 games with songs that accompany many of them; cross references to show similarities, differences among them; variations; musical notation for 38 songs. Textual discussions show relations with folk-drama and other aspects of folk tradition. Grouped into categories for ready comparative study: Love-games, histories, playing at work, human life, bird and beast, mythology, guessing-games, etc. New introduction covers relations of songs and dances to timeless heritage of folklore, biographical sketch of Newell, other pertinent data. A good source of inspiration for those in charge of groups of children and a valuable reference for anthropologists, sociologists, psychiatrists. Introduction by Carl Withers. New indexes of first lines, games. 5⅜ x 8½. xii + 242pp. **T354 Paperbound $1.65**

Art, History of Art, Antiques, Graphic Arts, Handcrafts

ART STUDENTS' ANATOMY, E. J. Farris. Outstanding art anatomy that uses chiefly living objects for its illustrations. 71 photos of undraped men, women, children are accompanied by carefully labeled matching sketches to illustrate the skeletal system, articulations and movements, bony landmarks, the muscular system, skin, fasciae, fat, etc. 9 x-ray photos show movement of joints. Undraped models are shown in such actions as serving in tennis, drawing a bow in archery, playing football, dancing, preparing to spring and to dive. Also discussed and illustrated are proportions, age and sex differences, the anatomy of the smile, etc. 8 plates by the great early 18th century anatomic illustrator Siegfried Albinus are also included. Glossary. 158 figures, 7 in color. x + 159pp. 5⅝ x 8⅜. T744 Paperbound **$1.45**

AN ATLAS OF ANATOMY FOR ARTISTS, F Schider. A new 3rd edition of this standard text enlarged by 52 new illustrations of hands, anatomical studies by Cloquet, and expressive life studies of the body by Barcsay. 189 clear, detailed plates offer you precise information of impeccable accuracy. 29 plates show all aspects of the skeleton, with closeups of special areas, while 54 full-page plates, mostly in two colors, give human musculature as seen from four different points of view, with cutaways for important portions of the body. 14 full-page plates provide photographs of hand forms, eyelids, female breasts, and indicate the location of muscles upon models. 59 additional plates show how great artists of the past utilized human anatomy. They reproduce sketches and finished work by such artists as Michelangelo, Leonardo da Vinci, Goya, and 15 others. This is a lifetime reference work which will be one of the most important books in any artist's library. "The standard reference tool," AMERICAN LIBRARY ASSOCIATION. "Excellent," AMERICAN ARTIST. Third enlarged edition. 189 plates, 647 illustrations. xxvi + 192pp. 7⅞ x 10⅝. T241 Clothbound **$6.00**

AN ATLAS OF ANIMAL ANATOMY FOR ARTISTS, W. Ellenberger, H. Baum, H. Dittrich. The largest, richest animal anatomy for artists available in English. 99 detailed anatomical plates of such animals as the horse, dog, cat, lion, deer, seal, kangaroo, flying squirrel, cow, bull, goat, monkey, hare, and bat. Surface features are clearly indicated, while progressive beneath-the-skin pictures show musculature, tendons, and bone structure. Rest and action are exhibited in terms of musculature and skeletal structure and detailed cross-sections are given for heads and important features. The animals chosen are representative of specific families so that a study of these anatomies will provide knowledge of hundreds of related species. "Highly recommended as one of the very few books on the subject worthy of being used as an authoritative guide," DESIGN. "Gives a fundamental knowledge," AMERICAN ARTIST. Second revised, enlarged edition with new plates from Cuvier, Stubbs, etc. 288 illustrations. 153pp. 11⅜ x 9. T82 Clothbound **$6.00**

THE HUMAN FIGURE IN MOTION, Eadweard Muybridge. The largest selection in print of Muybridge's famous high-speed action photos of the human figure in motion. 4789 photographs illustrate 162 different actions: men, women, children—mostly undraped—are shown walking, running, carrying various objects, sitting, lying down, climbing, throwing, arising, and performing over 150 other actions. Some actions are shown in as many as 150 photographs each. All in all there are more than 500 action strips in this enormous volume, series shots taken at shutter speeds of as high as 1/6000th of a second! These are not posed shots, but true stopped motion. They show bone and muscle in situations that the human eye is not fast enough to capture. Earlier, smaller editions of these prints have brought $40 and more on the out-of-print market. "A must for artists," ART IN FOCUS. "An unparalleled dictionary of action for all artists," AMERICAN ARTIST. 390 full-page plates, with 4789 photographs. Printed on heavy glossy stock. Reinforced binding with headbands. xxi + 390pp. 7⅞ x 10⅝. T204 Clothbound **$10.00**

ANIMALS IN MOTION, Eadweard Muybridge. This is the largest collection of animal action photos in print. 34 different animals (horses, mules, oxen, goats, camels, pigs, cats, guanacos, lions, gnus, deer, monkeys, eagles—and 21 others) in 132 characteristic actions. The horse alone is shown in more than 40 different actions. All 3919 photographs are taken in series at speeds up to 1/6000th of a second. The secrets of leg motion, spinal patterns, head movements, strains and contortions shown nowhere else are captured. You will see exactly how a lion sets his foot down; how an elephant's knees are like a human's—and how they differ; the position of a kangaroo's legs in mid-leap; how an ostrich's head bobs; details of the flight of birds—and thousands of facets of motion only the fastest cameras can catch. Photographed from domestic animals and animals in the Philadelphia zoo, it contains neither semiposed artificial shots nor distorted telephoto shots taken under adverse conditions. Artists, biologists, decorators, cartoonists, will find this book indispensable for understanding animals in motion. "A really marvelous series of plates," NATURE (London). "The dry plate's most spectacular early use was by Eadweard Muybridge," LIFE. 3919 photographs; 380 full pages of plates. 440pp. Printed on heavy glossy paper. Deluxe binding with headbands. 7⅞ x 10⅝. T203 Clothbound **$10.00**

CATALOGUE OF DOVER BOOKS

THE AUTOBIOGRAPHY OF AN IDEA, Louis Sullivan. The pioneer architect whom Frank Lloyd Wright called "the master" reveals an acute sensitivity to social forces and values in this passionately honest account. He records the crystallization of his opinions and theories, the growth of his organic theory of architecture that still influences American designers and architects, contemporary ideas, etc. This volume contains the first appearance of 34 full-page plates of his finest architecture. Unabridged reissue of 1924 edition. New introduction by R. M. Line. Index. xiv + 335pp. 5⅜ x 8.   **T281 Paperbound $2.00**

THE DRAWINGS OF HEINRICH KLEY. The first uncut republication of both of Kley's devastating sketchbooks, which first appeared in pre-World War I Germany. One of the greatest cartoonists and social satirists of modern times, his exuberant and iconoclastic fantasy and his extraordinary technique place him in the great tradition of Bosch, Breughel, and Goya, while his subject matter has all the immediacy and tension of our century. 200 drawings. viii + 128pp. 7¾ x 10¾.   **T24 Paperbound $1.85**

MORE DRAWINGS BY HEINRICH KLEY. All the sketches from Leut' Und Viecher (1912) and Sammel-Album (1923) not included in the previous Dover edition of Drawings. More of the bizarre, mercilessly iconoclastic sketches that shocked and amused on their original publication. Nothing was too sacred, no one too eminent for satirization by this imaginative, individual and accomplished master cartoonist. A total of 158 illustrations. Iv + 104pp. 7¾ x 10¾.   **T41 Paperbound $1.85**

PINE FURNITURE OF EARLY NEW ENGLAND, R. H. Kettell. A rich understanding of one of America's most original folk arts that collectors of antiques, interior decorators, craftsmen, woodworkers, and everyone interested in American history and art will find fascinating and immensely useful. 413 illustrations of more than 300 chairs, benches, racks, beds, cupboards, mirrors, shelves, tables, and other furniture will show all the simple beauty and character of early New England furniture. 55 detailed drawings carefully analyze outstanding pieces. "With its rich store of illustrations, this book emphasizes the individuality and varied design of early American pine furniture. It should be welcomed," ANTIQUES. 413 illustrations and 55 working drawings. 475. 8 x 10¾.   **T145 Clothbound $10.00**

THE HUMAN FIGURE, J. H. Vanderpoel. Every important artistic element of the human figure is pointed out in minutely detailed word descriptions in this classic text and illustrated as well in 430 pencil and charcoal drawings. Thus the text of this book directs your attention to all the characteristic features and subtle differences of the male and female (adults, children, and aged persons), as though a master artist were telling you what to look for at each stage. 2nd edition, revised and enlarged by George Bridgman. Foreword. 430 illustrations. 143pp. 6⅛ x 9¼.   **T432 Paperbound $1.50**

LETTERING AND ALPHABETS, J. A. Cavanagh. This unabridged reissue of LETTERING offers a full discussion, analysis, illustration of 89 basic hand lettering styles — styles derived from Caslons, Bodonis, Garamonds, Gothic, Black Letter, Oriental, and many others. Upper and lower cases, numerals and common signs pictured. Hundreds of technical hints on make-up, construction, artistic validity, strokes, pens, brushes, white areas, etc. May be reproduced without permission! 89 complete alphabets; 72 lettered specimens. 121pp. 9¾ x 8.
T53 Paperbound $1.25

STICKS AND STONES, Lewis Mumford. A survey of the forces that have conditioned American architecture and altered its forms. The author discusses the medieval tradition in early New England villages; the Renaissance influence which developed with the rise of the merchant class; the classical influence of Jefferson's time; the "Mechanicsvilles" of Poe's generation; the Brown Decades; the philosophy of the Imperial facade; and finally the modern machine age. "A truly remarkable book," SAT. REV. OF LITERATURE. 2nd revised edition. 21 illustrations. xvii + 228pp. 5⅜ x 8.   **T202 Paperbound $1.60**

THE STANDARD BOOK OF QUILT MAKING AND COLLECTING, Marguerite Ickis. A complete easy-to-follow guide with all the information you need to make beautiful, useful quilts. How to plan, design, cut, sew, appliqué, avoid sewing problems, use rag bag, make borders, tuft, every other aspect. Over 100 traditional quilts shown, including over 40 full-size patterns. At-home hobby for fun, profit. Index. 483 illus. 1 color plate. 287pp. 6¾ x 9½.
T582 Paperbound $2.00

THE BOOK OF SIGNS, Rudolf Koch. Formerly $20 to $25 on the out-of-print market, now only $1.00 in this unabridged new edition! 493 symbols from ancient manuscripts, medieval cathedrals, coins, catacombs, pottery, etc. Crosses, monograms of Roman emperors, astrological, chemical, botanical, runes, housemarks, and 7 other categories. Invaluable for handicraft workers, illustrators, scholars, etc., this material may be reproduced without permission. 493 illustrations by Fritz Kredel. 104pp. 6½ x 9¼.   **T162 Paperbound $1.00**

PRIMITIVE ART, Franz Boas. This authoritative and exhaustive work by a great American anthropologist covers the entire gamut of primitive art. Pottery, leatherwork, metal work, stone work, wood, basketry, are treated in detail. Theories of primitive art, historical depth in art history, technical virtuosity, unconscious levels of patterning, symbolism, styles, literature, music, dance, etc. A must book for the interested layman, the anthropologist, artist, handicrafter (hundreds of unusual motifs), and the historian. Over 900 illustrations (50 ceramic vessels, 12 totem poles, etc.). 376pp. 5⅜ x 8.   **T25 Paperbound $1.95**

Fiction

FLATLAND, E. A. Abbott. A science-fiction classic of life in a 2-dimensional world that is also a first-rate introduction to such aspects of modern science as relativity and hyperspace. Political, moral, satirical, and humorous overtones have made FLATLAND fascinating reading for thousands. 7th edition. New introduction by Banesh Hoffmann. 16 illustrations. 128pp. 5⅜ x 8. **T1 Paperbound $1.00**

THE WONDERFUL WIZARD OF OZ, L. F. Baum. Only edition in print with all the original W. W. Denslow illustrations in full color—as much a part of "The Wizard" as Tenniel's drawings are of "Alice in Wonderland." "The Wizard" is still America's best-loved fairy tale, in which, as the author expresses it, "The wonderment and joy are retained and the heartaches and nightmares left out." Now today's young readers can enjoy every word and wonderful picture of the original book. New introduction by Martin Gardner. A Baum bibliography. 23 full-page color plates. viii + 268pp. 5⅜ x 8. **T691 Paperbound $1.45**

THE MARVELOUS LAND OF OZ, L. F. Baum. This is the equally enchanting sequel to the "Wizard," continuing the adventures of the Scarecrow and the Tin Woodman. The hero this time is a little boy named Tip, and all the delightful Oz magic is still present. This is the Oz book with the Animated Saw-Horse, the Woggle-Bug, and Jack Pumpkinhead. All the original John R. Neill illustrations, 10 in full color. 287 pp. 5⅜ x 8. **T692 Paperbound $1.45**

FIVE GREAT DOG NOVELS, edited by Blanche Cirker. The complete original texts of five classic dog novels that have delighted and thrilled millions of children and adults throughout the world with their stories of loyalty, adventure, and courage. Full texts of Jack London's "The Call of the Wild"; John Brown's "Rab and His Friends"; Alfred Ollivant's "Bob, Son of Battle"; Marshall Saunders's "Beautiful Joe"; and Ouida's "A Dog of Flanders." 21 Illustrations from the original editions. 495pp. 5⅜ x 8. **T777 Paperbound $1.50**

TO THE SUN? and OFF ON A COMET!, Jules Verne. Complete texts of two of the most imaginative flights into fancy in world literature display the high adventure that have kept Verne's novels read for nearly a century. Only unabridged edition of the best translation, by Edward Roth. Large, easily readable type. 50 illustrations selected from first editions. 462pp. 5⅜ x 8. **T634 Paperbound $1.75**

FROM THE EARTH TO THE MOON and ALL AROUND THE MOON, Jules Verne. Complete editions of 2 of Verne's most successful novels, in finest Edward Roth translations, now available after many years out of print. Verne's visions of submarines, airplanes, television, rockets, interplanetary travel; of scientific and not-so-scientific beliefs; of peculiarities of Americans; all delight and engross us today as much as when they first appeared. Large, easily readable type. 42 illus. from first French edition. 476pp. 5⅜ x 8. **T633 Paperbound $1.75**

THE CRUISE OF THE CACHALOT, Frank T. Bullen. Out of the experiences of many years on the high-seas, First Mate Bullen created this novel of adventure aboard an American whaler, shipping out of New Bedford, Mass., when American whaling was at the height of its splendor. Originally published in 1899, the story of the round-the-world cruise of the "Cachalot" in pursuit of the sperm whale has thrilled generations of readers. A maritime classic that will fascinate anyone interested in reading about the sea or looking for a solid old-fashioned yarn, while the vivid recreation of a brief but important chapter of Americana and the British author's often biting commentary on nineteenth-century Yankee mores offer insights into the colorful era of America's coming of age. 8 plates. xiii + 271pp. 5⅜ x 8½. **T774 Paperbound $1.00**

28 SCIENCE FICTION STORIES OF H. G. WELLS. Two full unabridged novels, MEN LIKE GODS and STAR BEGOTTEN, plus 26 short stories by the master science-fiction writer of all time! Stories of space, time, invention, exploration, future adventure—an indispensable part of the library of everyone interested in science and adventure. PARTIAL CONTENTS: Men Like Gods, The Country of the Blind, In the Abyss, The Crystal Egg, The Man Who Could Work Miracles, A Story of the Days to Come, The Valley of Spiders, and 21 more! 928pp. 5⅜ x 8. **T265 Clothbound $3.95**

DAVID HARUM, E. N. Westcott. This novel of one of the most lovable, humorous characters in American literature is a prime example of regional humor. It continues to delight people who like their humor dry, their characters quaint, and their plots ingenuous. First book edition to contain complete novel plus chapter found after author's death. Illustrations from first illustrated edition. 192pp. 5⅜ x 8. **T580 Paperbound $1.15**

GESTA ROMANORUM, trans. by Charles Swan, ed. by Wynnard Hooper. 181 tales of Greeks, Romans, Britons, Biblical characters, comprise one of greatest medieval story collections, source of plots for writers including Shakespeare, Chaucer, Gower, etc. Imaginative tales of wars, incest, thwarted love, magic, fantasy, allegory, humor, tell about kings, prostitutes, philosophers, fair damsels, knights, Noah, pirates, all walks, stations of life. Introduction. Notes. 500pp. 5⅜ x 8. **T535 Paperbound $1.85**

Music

A GENERAL HISTORY OF MUSIC, Charles Burney. A detailed coverage of music from the Greeks up to 1789, with full information on all types of music: sacred and secular, vocal and instrumental, operatic and symphonic. Theory, notation, forms, instruments, innovators, composers, performers, typical and important works, and much more in an easy, entertaining style. Burney covered much of Europe and spoke with hundreds of authorities and composers so that this work is more than a compilation of records . . . it is a living work of careful and first-hand scholarship. Its account of thoroughbass (18th century) Italian music is probably still the best introduction on the subject. A recent NEW YORK TIMES review said, "Surprisingly few of Burney's statements have been invalidated by modern research . . . still of great value." Edited and corrected by Frank Mercer. 35 figures. Indices. 1915pp. 5⅜ x 8. 2 volumes.   T36 The Set, Clothbound $12.50

A DICTIONARY OF HYMNOLOGY, John Julian. This exhaustive and scholarly work has become known as an invaluable source of hundreds of thousands of important and often difficult to obtain facts on the history and use of hymns in the western world. Everyone interested in hymns will be fascinated by the accounts of famous hymns and hymn writers and amazed by the amount of practical information he will find. More than 30,000 entries on individual hymns, giving authorship, date and circumstances of composition, publication, textual variations, translations, denominational and ritual usage, etc. Biographies of more than 9,000 hymn writers, and essays on important topics such as Christmas carols and children's hymns, and much other unusual and valuable information. A 200 page double-columned index of first lines — the largest in print. Total of 1786 pages in two reinforced clothbound volumes. 6¼ x 9¼.
The set, T333 Clothbound $15.00

MUSIC IN MEDIEVAL BRITAIN, F. Ll. Harrison. The most thorough, up-to-date, and accurate treatment of the subject ever published, beautifully illustrated. Complete account of institutions and choirs; carols, masses, and motets; liturgy and plainsong; and polyphonic music from the Norman Conquest to the Reformation. Discusses the various schools of music and their reciprocal influences; the origin and development of new ritual forms; development and use of instruments; and new evidence on many problems of the period. Reproductions of scores, over 200 excerpts from medieval melodies. Rules of harmony and dissonance; influence of Continental styles; great composers (Dunstable, Cornysh, Fairfax, etc.); and much more. Register and index of more than 400 musicians. Index of titles. General Index. 225-item bibliography. 6 Appendices. xix + 491pp. 5⅝ x 8¾.   T705 Clothbound $10.00

THE MUSIC OF SPAIN, Gilbert Chase. Only book in English to give concise, comprehensive account of Iberian music; new Chapter covers music since 1941. Victoria, Albéniz, Cabezón, Pedrell, Turina, hundreds of other composers; popular and folk music; the Gypsies; the guitar; dance, theatre, opera, with only extensive discussion in English of the Zarzuela; virtuosi such as Casals; much more. "Distinguished . . . readable," Saturday Review. 400-item bibliography. Index. 27 photos. 383pp. 5⅜ x 8.   T549 Paperbound $2.00

ON STUDYING SINGING, Sergius Kagen. An intelligent method of voice-training, which leads you around pitfalls that waste your time, money, and effort. Exposes rigid, mechanical systems, baseless theories, deleterious exercises. "Logical, clear, convincing . . . dead right," Virgil Thomson, N.Y. Herald Tribune. "I recommend this volume highly," Maggie Teyte, Saturday Review. 119pp. 5⅜ x 8.   T622 Paperbound $1.25

Dover publishes books on art, music, philosophy, literature, languages, history, social sciences, psychology, handcrafts, orientalia, puzzles and entertainments, chess, pets and gardens, books explaining science, intermediate and higher mathematics mathematical physics, engineering, biological sciences, earth sciences, classics of science, etc. Write to:

Dept. catrr.
Dover Publications, Inc.
180 Varick Street, N. Y. 14, N. Y.